The
As the World Turns
Quiz Book

The
As the World Turns
Quiz Book

Celebrating Forty Years of the Popular Soap Opera

Gerard J. Waggett

A Citadel Press Book
Published by Carol Publishing Group

A Citadel Press Book
Published by Carol Publishing Group
Citadel Press is a registered trademark of Carol Communications, Inc.
Editorial, sales and distribution, rights and permissions inquiries should be addressed to Carol Publishing Group, 120 Enterprise Avenue, Secaucus, N.J. 07094
In Canada: Canadian Manda Group, One Atlantic Avenue, Suite 105, Toronto, Ontario M6K 3E7

Carol Publishing Group books are available at special discounts for bulk purchases, sales promotion, fund-raising, or educational purposes. Special editions can be created to specifications. For details, contact: Special Sales Department, Carol Publishing Group, 120 Enterprise Avenue, Secaucus, N.J. 07094

Manufactured in the United States of America
10 9 8 7 6 5 4 3 2 1

Library of Congress Cataloging-in-Publication Data

Waggett, Gerard J.
     The As the world turns quiz book : celebrating forty years of the popular soap opera / Gerard J. Waggett.
        p. cm.
     "A Citadel Press book."
     ISBN 0-8065-1808-1 (pbk.)
     1. As the world turns (Television program)—Miscellanea.
I. Title.
PN1992.77.A8W35   1996
791.45′72—dc20   96-26770
                                                                CIP

Happy Birthday, Mom

Acknowledgments

A number of people helped make this book a reality, and I would like to thank them here for their efforts: my editor Allan J. Wilson, who gave this project the green light, and my agents, Frank Coffey and Frank Weimann, who put the car on the road. I would also like to thank Connie Walsh, R. Scott Reedy, Karen Lindsey, and Don Casali for their much-needed feedback and insight. As always, I have to thank my family for their continued support: my mother, Barbara Waggett (who shares her birthday with *As the World Turns*'s anniversary), my father, Frederick Waggett, my aunt, Margaret Connolly, my uncles Jackie and Eddie Connolly, and my cousin Mabel Waggett. While I thank all my friends for their continued support, I need to single out one special friend in particular: Eileen Maher, who took a crash course in *As the World Turns* history to become my research assistant and help me get this book wrapped up in time to celebrate Christmas.

A Tip Sheet for Solving These Quizzes

For those fans (like myself) who have not been watching *As the World Turns* since its premiere episode back in 1956, I put together the following tip sheet. It should come in handy for tackling the multiple-choice questions that comprise so many of the quizzes in this book.

1. If a question asks how someone died suddenly before 1975, your best bet is to pick something to do with a car accident. Back in the late fifties and early sixties, when widows were a lot more sympathetic than divorcées, car accidents really were the preferred method of ending a marriage.

2. If the question is asking about how a character died from some medical condition before 1975, always choose the vaguest answer on the list. The key word to keep an eye out for is "unspecified" (as in "an unspecified blood disease" or "an unspecified neurological condition"). Brain tumors were also popular during this time because the length of the illness could be so easily adjusted to fit the needs of the plotline.

3. When you're playing Trivial Pursuit, you usually can't go too wrong guessing John F. Kennedy as an answer. The same holds true here for Lisa Miller, who's been involved with almost everybody in Oakdale in some way or another for the past thirty-six years. Lisa is a pretty safe guess for just about any question that doesn't begin with the words "Who fathered."

4. For those questions that do begin with the words, "Who fathered," the prolific John Dixon is probably your surest bet. He has had four different children with four different women so far. Six times divorced, he is also a good guess for those questions that begin with the words "Who married."

5. When you're asked to identify who a certain character's

father is, don't try to match up the last names. More often than not, you'd be better off using matching last names as a way of eliminating a selection.

6. Some of the questions in the book are going to ask why a certain hero or heroine did something totally out of character. For instance, why did one heroine let her stepmother stand trial for murder when she'd seen who the real killer was? Or why did a respected doctor desert his family and become a druggist in a nearby town? In these cases, always go with the most obvious answer: amnesia.

7. A caveat regarding murder mysteries: Don't fall into the easy trap that the Oakdale Police Department always does of assuming that the victim is really dead.

8. Another caveat regarding murder mysteries: Who committed a murder and who went on trial for it will seldom be the same person.

9. On the quizzes about James Stenbeck, try to spell out the word "CAD" as much as you can with the multiple-choice answers.

10. If you really get stuck for an answer, take a hint from the people you're reading about—the Lisa Millers, the James Stenbecks, and the John Dixons: Cheat. The answers are in the back of the book.

The
As the World Turns
Quiz Book

The Beginning of the World

As the World Turns debuted on April 2, 1956. It has been on the air for the past forty years, making it the second longest running soap opera in television history. *(Guiding Light,* which began on TV in 1952, is number one.) The following quiz will take you back to the very beginning of the show.

1. What was *As the World Turns* the first soap opera to do?
   a. air in color
   b. make a successful transition from radio to television
   c. tape in Los Angeles
   d. debut as a half-hour soap

2. From what soap opera was *As the World Turns* a spin-off?
   a. *The Guiding Light*
   b. *The Secret Storm*
   c. the radio soap *Pepper Young's Family*
   d. It wasn't a spin-off.

3. What other soap opera also made its debut on April 2, 1956?
   a. *Love of Life*
   b. *The Edge of Night*
   c. *General Hospital*
   d. *Search for Tomorrow*

4. Which current soap opera legend was Irna Phillips's first headwriter?
   a. Agnes Nixon
   b. Bill Bell
   c. Harding Lemay
   d. Douglas Marland

5. What future *Days of Our Lives* cocreator (with Phillips) served as the show's first director?
   a. Gloria Monty
   b. Bill Bell
   c. Ted Corday
   d. H. Wesley Kenney

6. Creator Irna Phillips knew that *As the World Turns* would start off slowly and needed time to build an audience. She also knew that Procter & Gamble did not share her enthusiasm for the project. Nevertheless, she negotiated a contract with Procter & Gamble that guaranteed the show would stay on the air for a minimum of how long?
   a. thirteen weeks
   b. six months
   c. one year
   d. two years

7. What were the first words spoken on the show?
   a. "Good morning."
   b. "Where have you been?"
   c. "Oh my God. Get a doctor."
   d. "Welcome to Oakdale."

8. Which character spoke those words?
   a. Chris Hughes
   b. Nancy Hughes
   c. Bob Hughes
   d. Penny Hughes

9. Thirteen weeks into the show, Helen Wagner was fired by Irna Phillips. What reason did Phillips give for firing her? (Phillips, it should be noted, regretted her decision shortly after firing Wagner and hired her back as soon as she could.)
   a. Phillips thought Wagner looked too young onscreen to be playing a mother.
   b. Phillips claimed that Wagner couldn't remember her lines.

    c. Wagner announced that she was pregnant in real life.

    d. Phillips didn't like the way Wagner wore her hair or her clothes.

10. Like Wagner, Hal Struder, who created the role of Donald Hughes, was fired during the first year. Unlike Wagner, though, he was not rehired. What reason did Phillips give for firing Hal Struder?

    a. He looked too short onscreen.

    b. He looked too heavy onscreen.

    c. He tended to stutter during emotional scenes.

    d. He grew a mustache.

11. How many children did Nancy and Chris Hughes have?

    a. two

    b. three

    c. four

    d. five

12. How did Chris and Nancy's daughter Susan die during the first year?

    a. Her radio fell into the tub while she was taking a bath.

    b. She fell out of a tree and hit her head.

    c. She was struck by lightning while swimming.

    d. She choked to death on Halloween candy.

13. What was Grandpa Hughes's seldom used first name?

    a. Christopher

    b. Bob

    c. Donald

    d. Will

14. During the show's first year, the main story line was the adulterous affair between Jim Lowell and Edith Hughes. Although Irna Phillips wanted Jim Lowell to divorce his wife, Claire, and marry Edith, she didn't go through with that idea. Instead, she killed him off in a boating accident. What made her change the story line?
   a. Procter & Gamble objected to Jim marrying Edith.
   b. Ruth Warrick, who played Edith, announced that she was leaving the show.
   c. Les Damon, who played Jim, announced that he was leaving.
   d. It was too similar to a plot twist being used on *The Guiding Light.*

15. Where did *As the World Turns* rank in popularity among the daytime soaps during its first year on the air?
   a. first place
   b. second place
   c. third place
   d. last place

As *TV Guide* Summed It Up...

When *As the World Turns* debuted back in 1956, *TV Guide* summed the show up in a two-sentence blurb that ran under its listing the very first day. To figure out how *TV Guide* described the show, you have to break the code. Remember that each letter stands for one and only one other letter. (One hint: two of the show's stars are mentioned by name in the blurb.)

DRAN HGDDEVT OAGDO EQ G QXH LGECF

NGCJ-NZRD LDGYGAEV OXDEXO LXGCEQW

HEAN ANX IDZUCXYO GQL

GVVZYICEONYXQAO ZJ G JGYECF LZQ

YGVCGRWNCEQ [GCOZ OAGDO].

Lisa Miller Hughes, et cetera: The Early Years

When Eileen Fulton was first hired to play the conniving Lisa Miller, the role was only supposed to last a few days. She would come on as Bob Hughes's girlfriend and then leave. The writers, however, saw potential in Fulton and expanded the role. With the departure of Ruth Warrick as the adulterous Edith Hughes, the show needed a shady lady to create some tension. By the mid 1960s, Lisa was the most popular character on the soaps.

1. Where did Lisa come from?
    a. New York City
    b. Savannah, Georgia
    c. Topeka, Kansas
    d. Rockford, Illinois

2. Lisa grew up...
    a. on a farm.
    b. in an orphanage.
    c. shuttled between relatives.
    d. in a trailer park.

3. What was Lisa's mother's name?
   a. Alma
   b. Barbara
   c. Margaret
   d. Mabel

4. Where did Lisa meet Bob Hughes?
   a. at the hospital
   b. in England
   c. in college
   d. through his sister Penny

5. After Bob eloped with Lisa, his parents, Chris and Nancy, wanted to have the marriage annulled. Why did they change their minds?
   a. Lisa's mother died, leaving her all alone in the world.
   b. Bob threatened to quit medical school if they interfered with his marriage.
   c. Lisa blackmailed them into accepting her.
   d. Lisa was already pregnant.

6. Where did Bob and Lisa live when they were first married?
   a. in a one-room apartment
   b. at the college dorm
   c. with Chris and Nancy
   d. in a trailer park right outside Oakdale

7. With whom did Lisa have an affair while married to Bob?
   a. Doug Cassen
   b. Bruce Elliot
   c. Carl Whipple
   d. Donald Hughes

8. Why did Lisa's lover refuse to marry her?
   a. She wasn't sophisticated enough for him.
   b. He owed Bob Hughes for saving his life.
   c. His ex-wife wanted him back.

d. Nancy Hughes threatened to ruin his reputation if he didn't drop Lisa.

9. What event made Lisa regret the way she'd treated Bob and prompted her to seek a reconciliation with him?
   a. Bob attempted suicide.
   b. Bob was hit by a car.
   c. Their son Tom got sick and almost died.
   d. Tom ran away from home and was missing for two days.

10. When Bob refused to take Lisa back, where did she head off to?
   a. Las Vegas
   b. Chicago
   c. Hollywood
   d. England

In Another Life

Although soap actors do tend to become identified with a specific character, it is not uncommon for them to move around daytime, trying on new costumes, so to speak. At least ten of the actors currently on *As the World Turns* began their soap careers elsewhere. As you will notice, many of the current actors and actresses came to the show from other Procter & Gamble programs: *The Guiding Light, Another World, Texas,* and *The Edge of Night.* All you have to do is match each current *As the World Turns* cast member with his or her previous soap role.

1. Don Hastings (Bob Hughes)
2. Helen Wagner (Nancy Hughes McCloskey)
3. Scott Holmes (Tom Hughes)

a. Rose Perrini, *Another World*
b. Joe Foster, *Texas*
c. Leslie Jackson, *Guiding Light*

4. Ellen Dolan (Margo Hughes)

5. Patrick Tovatt (Cal Stricklyn)

6. Kathryn Hays (Kim Hughes)

7. Benjamin Hendrickson (Hal Munson)

8. Kathleen Widdoes (Emma Snyder)

9. Tom Wiggin (Kirk Anderson)

10. Elizabeth Hubbard (Lucinda Walsh)

d. Silas Crocker, *Guiding Light*

e. Trudy Bauer, *Guiding Light*

f. Dave Greenberg, *Ryan's Hope*

g. Althea Davis, *The Doctors*

h. Jack Lane, *The Edge of Night*

i. Maureen Bauer, *Guiding Light*

j. Zane Lindquist, *Another World*

Ellen's Sordid Past

It is no wonder that Ellen Stewart (currently played by Patricia Bruder) can sympathize with her less than saintly granddaughter Emily. Although Ellen is considered by many in Oakdale to be a paragon of virtue, in her youth she would have been described as anything but. Ellen's early years were riddled with adultery, a subsequent out-of-wedlock pregnancy, and even a prison sentence.

1. Although Ellen was deeply disturbed by her father's infidelity, she herself entered into an affair with a married doctor. What was his name?
   a. Al James
   b. Bob Hughes
   c. Tim Cole
   d. John Dixon

2. Ellen wound up pregnant as a result of that affair. What did she name the baby?
   a. Jeff
   b. Jimmy
   c. Tom
   d. She named him after his father.

3. What prompted Ellen to give the baby up for adoption?
   a. Other mothers in the park refused to sit near Ellen and her baby.
   b. Ellen's mother cut off her financial support.
   c. Ellen's fiancée broke up with her when he discovered she had a child.
   d. Ellen was accepted to college in another state.

4. What did the adoptive parents, David and Betty Stewart, rename Ellen's baby?
   a. Dan
   b. Paul
   c. Rod
   d. David Junior

5. Ellen changed her mind about the adoption and and sued the Stewarts to get her son back. Who represented her in the case?
   a. Donald Hughes
   b. Chris Hughes
   c. Her father, James
   d. She represented herself.

6. Which member of Ellen's family suffered a heart attack after testifying against her during the case?
   a. her father, James
   b. her mother, Claire
   c. her stepfather, Doug Cassen
   d. her grandfather, Judge Lowell

7. What event occurred shortly after Ellen lost the case that resulted in her taking a more active role in the raising of her son?
   a. Betty Stewart died.
   b. Betty Stewart suffered a stroke.
   c. Betty Stewart left David for another man.
   d. Betty Stewart had to be committed to a sanitarium.

8. What objection did David's housekeeper Franny Brennan have to the relationship that developed between David and Ellen?
   a. Franny was in love with David and wanted him for herself.
   b. Franny had been married to the doctor with whom Ellen had her affair.
   c. Franny believed that Ellen was a horrible mother and should not be near the baby.
   d. Ellen's mother was paying Franny to keep David and Ellen apart.

9. What did Franny threaten to do if Ellen married David?
   a. ruin David's reputation and his career
   b. tell Ellen's son the truth about his conception
   c. report Ellen to social services as an unfit mother
   d. kill Ellen

10. Ellen went to prison for killing Franny during an argument. With what did Ellen hit Franny over the head?
    a. a small statue
    b. a baseball bat
    c. a candlestick
    d. a lead pipe

Love That Bob

Marriage to a vixen like Lisa Miller might have scared some men away from ever getting hitched again. But not Bob Hughes. In the thirty-plus years since his divorce from Lisa, Bob has gone on to marry again and again and again and yet again. The following quiz concentrates on Wives Number 2 through 4 as well as a couple of women he almost walked down the aisle. As you'll note, Bob didn't learn nearly as much as he should have from his disastrous marriage to Lisa.

1. After Bob divorced Lisa, he became involved with a nurse named Sylvia Hill. From what potentially life-threatening disease did Sylvia suffer?
   a. asthma
   b. hypoglycemia
   c. lupus
   d. diabetes

2. After Bob divorced Lisa, Ellen Lowell Stewart introduced him to Sandy McGuire. How did Ellen know Sandy?
   a. Sandy showed up in town claiming to be Jim Lowell's daughter.
   b. They had both been taken hostage in a bank holdup.
   c. They had both served time in the same prison.
   d. Ellen's mother had married Sandy's father.

3. Sandy had married Bob for financial security for herself and her son Jimmy. The marriage, as expected, didn't last. After it broke up, Sandy moved to New York to try her hand at what profession?
   a. acting
   b. modeling
   c. dancing
   d. fashion design

4. Bob's third wife was Jennifer Ryan. How had Bob known Jennifer's late husband?
   a. They had gone to medical school together.
   b. They had served in the army together.
   c. He had been a business acquaintance of Bob's father.
   d. Bob had treated him for a heart condition.

5. Who caused so much tension between Jennifer and Bob that he ended up leaving her?

   a. John Dixon
   b. Jennifer's daughter Barbara
   c. Jennifer's son Rick
   d. the "ghost" of Jennifer's late husband

6. With whom did Bob have an affair while separated from Jennifer?

   a. her sister Kim
   b. Lisa
   c. Susan Stewart
   d. Joyce Colman

7. What medical secret did Bob keep from Jennifer?

   a. She was going blind.
   b. Their baby was born with a life-threatening birth defect.
   c. Rick was not her late husband's biological son.
   d. She was dying of a neurological illness.

8. How did Jennifer die?

   a. She died in a fire.
   b. She fell down a flight of stairs.
   c. She was killed in a car accident.
   d. John Dixon prescribed the wrong medication for her heart condition.

9. Why did Bob break his engagement to Lyla Montgomery?

   a. She was already married to another man.
   b. He caught her stealing drugs from the hospital.
   c. He learned that she had had an affair with John Dixon while living in Chicago.
   d. She slept with his brother Donald.

10. For what crime did Bob's fourth wife, Miranda Marlowe serve time in prison?
    a. arson
    b. blackmail
    c. counterfeiting
    d. drug trafficking

A Penny for Your Thoughts

Penny Hughes, played by Rosemary Prinz, was not only *As the World Turns*'s first teen heroine, she was daytime's first—long before youth-oriented story lines became the norm. During Prinz's twelve years on the show, Penny caused her parents and ultimately herself a great deal of grief with her impetuous and ill-planned marriages, two of which left her a young widow.

1. Why did Penny envy her sister Susan?
    a. Penny loved Jeff Baker, who preferred Susan.
    b. Susan was more beautiful and worked as a model.
    c. Penny believed that their mother Nancy loved Susan more.
    d. Susan had been accepted to Radcliffe College.

2. Why did Chris and Nancy object to Penny's relationship with Jeff Baker?
    a. Jeff was married.
    b. Jeff was a wild rich boy, and Penny was too young for any serious involvement.
    c. Penny had stolen Jeff away from Susan, who had planned on marrying him.
    d. The Baker Family had a long-standing feud with the Hugheses.

3. Her parents' disapproval pushed Penny into running away with Jeff to get married. How did Chris and Nancy handle the elopement?
   a. They stopped the wedding right before Penny could say, "I do."
   b. They had the wedding annulled.
   c. They forced Penny to get a divorce.
   d. They allowed Penny and Jeff to stay married but refused to permit them to live together.

4. After Jeff straightened up his act, Chris and Nancy gave their blessing to a wedding between Jeff and Penny. On what holiday in 1959 did Jeff and Penny marry?
   a. Valentine's Day
   b. Easter
   c. Christmas Eve
   d. New Year's Eve

5. What disturbing medical news did Penny learn shortly after the wedding?
   a. She could never have children.
   b. She was pregnant by another man.
   c. She was diabetic.
   d. She needed a kidney transplant.

6. Not too long into Penny and Jeff's marriage, Mark Rydell (who played Jeff) decided to leave the show. Rather than recasting the role, the decision was made that Jeff would simply be killed off. How did he die?
   a. He was shot by a mugger.
   b. He developed a brain tumor.
   c. He was in a car accident.
   d. He drowned.

7. Penny's next husband, Neil Wade, was a doctor who eventually gave up practicing medicine. Which character did he discover was his biological father?
   a. Judge Lowell
   b. David Stewart
   c. Jeff's father Al Baker
   d. Doug Cassen

8. What sort of business did Penny and Neil open up together?
   a. a restaurant
   b. a bookstore
   c. a movie theater
   d. a veterinary clinic

9. How did Neil ultimately die?
   a. He was trapped inside a burning house.
   b. He was bitten by a rattlesnake.
   c. He took an accidental overdose of pain medication.
   d. He was hit by a car.

10. After Neil's death, Penny had a short-lived marriage to Roy McGuire. How did they know each other?
   a. Roy was Jeff Baker's half brother.
   b. Roy's ex-wife Sandy had been married to Penny's brother Bob.
   c. Roy worked for Penny's father.
   d. Roy had been Neil's doctor.

Lisa's Husband Search

Throughout the past 36 years, Eileen Fulton's Lisa has gone hunting for many a husband. To date, she has been married a total of seven times and has had more husbands than any other soap opera heroine or vixen. (While *All My Children*'s Erica Kane has been married more often, Erica tends to marry the men twice and illegally.) Hidden in the letter board below are the names of all seven of Lisa's husbands. To make things a little more challenging, you have to remember the names of all those husbands yourself.

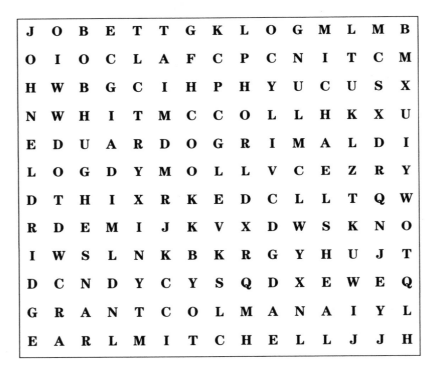

J	O	B	E	T	T	G	K	L	O	G	M	L	M	B
O	I	O	C	L	A	F	C	P	C	N	I	T	C	M
H	W	B	G	C	I	H	P	H	Y	U	C	U	S	X
N	W	H	I	T	M	C	C	O	L	L	H	K	X	U
E	D	U	A	R	D	O	G	R	I	M	A	L	D	I
L	O	G	D	Y	M	O	L	L	V	C	E	Z	R	Y
D	T	H	I	X	R	K	E	D	C	L	L	T	Q	W
R	D	E	M	I	J	K	V	X	D	W	S	K	N	O
I	W	S	L	N	K	B	K	R	G	Y	H	U	J	T
D	C	N	D	Y	C	Y	S	Q	D	X	E	W	E	Q
G	R	A	N	T	C	O	L	M	A	N	A	I	Y	L
E	A	R	L	M	I	T	C	H	E	L	L	J	J	H

The First Lady of Daytime

Christopher Schemering's *Soap Opera Encyclopedia* hails *As the World Turns*'s creator Irna Phillips as "the single most important force in creating what we now call 'soap opera.'" Between radio and television, she created or cocreated more than a dozen soap operas—four of which, including *As the World Turns*, are still on the air today. Although her career was marked by many triumphs, it ended on a low point, in 1973: She was fired from *As the World Turns* and died later that same year.

1. What career had Phillips dreamed of pursuing before she decided to become a writer?
   a. actress
   b. fashion designer
   c. singer
   d. doctor

2. What occupation did Phillips have in common with *As the World Turns*'s Nancy Hughes?
   a. maid
   b. nurse
   c. teacher
   d. newspaper reporter

3. Although the soaps she created were taped in New York City, Phillips did not live there. Where did she live while writing her soaps?
   a. Atlanta
   b. Boston
   c. Chicago
   d. Detroit

4. Phillips gave Bill Bell (creator of *The Young and the Restless* and *The Bold and the Beautiful*) his start in daytime and hired him as her second headwriter on *As the World Turns*. Where had she discovered Bell?
   a. He took a creative writing class she taught.
   b. He was her lawyer.
   c. He owned the apartment building she lived in.
   d. He was the messenger who delivered her scripts to the post office each day.

5. In the mid 1960s Phillips ventured into prime time, serving as a story consultant on what drama series?
   a. *Doctor Kildare*
   b. *The Fugitive*
   c. *Peyton Place*
   d. *Ben Casey*

6. Which *As the World Turns* character did Phillips model after herself?
   a. Nancy Hughes
   b. Kim Reynolds Hughes
   c. Lisa Miller
   d. Ellen Stewart

7. What short-lived soaps opera was created by Phillips's adopted daughter Katherine and was based upon Irna Phillips's own life?
   a. *A Woman to Remember*
   b. *Valiant Lady*
   c. *Our Private World*
   d. *A World Apart*

8. Which of the following idiosyncrasies did Phillips employ when speaking with an actor on the show?
   a. She would make the actor sit while she stood over him or her.
   b. She would address the actor only by his or her character's name.
   c. Actors had to refer to her as "Mother Irna."
   d. She would never speak to an actor without at least two witnesses present.

9. What story line prompted such negative viewer reaction and ratings loss that Procter & Gamble fired Phillips as head writer in 1973?
   a. The untimely death of Liz Talbot Stewart.
   b. Bob's affair with his sister-in-law Kim.
   c. Susan Stewart's alcoholism.
   d. Lisa's transformation from villainess to victim.

10. Which of the following current soap operas was not created or cocreated by Irna Phillips?
    a. *One Life to Live*
    b. *Another World*

c. *Guiding Light*
d. *Days of Our Lives*

The Prime-Time Spin-Off

In an attempt to capitalize on the success of the ABC hit *Peyton Place*, CBS decided to develop its own prime-time soap opera. The immense popularity of *As the World Turns* and of Eileen Fulton's performance as Lisa looked like a strong foundation to build upon. So, on May 3, 1965, Lisa boarded a train leaving Oakdale and was spun off into the prime-time serial *Our Private World*.

1. In what real-life city was *Our Private World* set?
    a. New York
    b. San Francisco
    c. Chicago
    d. Los Angeles

2. How many nights a week did the show air?
    a. one
    b. two
    c. three
    d. five

3. How did Lisa get rid of her wedding ring during the first scene?
    a. She tossed it out the window.
    b. She gave it to a panhandler.
    c. She hawked it at a pawnshop.
    d. She threw it away in her ashtray.

4. Which of her husbands did Lisa meet on the series?
    a. Michael Shea
    b. Whit McColl
    c. John Eldridge
    d. Grant Colman

5. How long did the series run?
   a. one month
   b. just through the summer
   c. one season
   d. two seasons

The Marriage Route

One of the more popular jokes about soap operas is that everybody in town is related by marriage to everybody else. There is some kernel of truth to that joke, as the following puzzle illustrates. Original cast member Jim Lowell is connected to the recently departed Larry McDermott through a series of marriages. In other words, Jim Lowell's wife married somebody who married somebody who married somebody and so on until you get down to Larry McDermott (who also happens to be the biological father to Jim's great-great-granddaughter). All you have do is fill in the appropriate spouses' names in the blanks provided. The marriages, it should be noted, do not always follow chronological order and occasionally seem to defy any logical order of any sort.

Jim Lowell was married to _____

who, after Jim's death, married and divorced _____

who later married _____

who had previously been married to _____

who is currently married to _____

who was widowed by _____

who had once been married to _____

who later married and recently separated from **Larry McDermott**.

Lisa Miller Hughes, et cetera: Shea's Rebellion

In Michael Shea (played by Jay Lanin and later by Roy Shuman), Lisa Miller finally met her match, a character who could be just as wicked as she was. Their tempestuous relationship started off as a passionate affair but deteriorated over the years into a bitter marriage that finally ended in 1970 with Michael's murder. Eileen Fulton considers it one of her all-time favorite story lines.

1. What was Michael Shea's profession?
   a. architect
   b. business executive
   c. cop
   d. doctor

2. To whom was he married when he began his affair with Lisa?
   a. Ellen
   b. Janice
   c. Claire
   d. Louise

3. Lisa, of course, expected Michael to divorce his wife, but Michael refused because his wife was...
   a. rich and socially prominent.
   b. connected to organized crime.
   c. threatening suicide.
   d. in a wheelchair because of him.

4. When Lisa gave birth to Michael's son, what did she name him?
   a. Michael Jr.
   b. Bob Jr.
   c. Chuckie
   d. Scott

5. What made Michael change his mind about marrying Lisa?
   a. He needed to keep her from testifying against him in court.
   b. He wanted to get back at Bob Hughes.
   c. He discovered that Lisa had come into a large inheritance.
   d. He decided that he wanted to raise their son.

6. By the time Michael decided he wanted to marry Lisa, she wanted nothing to do with him. What role did Tom play in Lisa's ultimately agreeing to marry Michael?
   a. Michael had caught Tom stealing drugs and blackmailed Lisa into marriage.
   b. Lisa needed to be married to Michael to better her chances for winning custody of Tom.
   c. Michael had saved Tom's life, and Lisa felt that she owed him.
   d. Tom looked upon Michael as a father figure.

7. What did Michael do to drive Lisa out of town?
   a. He tried to rape her.
   b. He became physically abusive.
   c. He made her believe that someone was trying to kill her.
   d. He threatened to prove her an unfit mother and get sole custody of their son.

8. To which country did Lisa run away?
   a. Mexico
   b. England
   c. Canada
   d. Greece

9. What brought Lisa back to Oakdale?
   a. Grandpa Hughes died.
   b. Tom had attempted suicide.
   c. Tom needed a kidney transplant.
   d. Her mother was ill.

10. When Lisa returned, she learned that Michael Shea had been killed. Although a disgruntled former lover had done him in, who thought that Lisa had killed Michael and took the blame to protect her?

   a. Tom

   b. Bob

   c. her mother

   d. Nancy

Bob and Kim

While Bob and Kim Hughes have settled into the role of Oakdale's first couple, their history together has been anything but tame. Bob first met Kim while he was getting married to her sister Jennifer. Although they fell in love at first sight, it took Bob and Kim more than a dozen years and a handful of marriages to other people before they ended up together.

1. Where did Bob and Kim's brief affair take place?

2. Why didn't Kim tell Bob that she was pregnant as a result of that affair?

3. What happened to Kim and Bob's first baby?

4. What happened to Bob on the day that Kim married John Dixon?

5. Although Bob and Kim went on to marry other people, they remained close friends. What happened in 1984 that triggered Bob's feelings to turn romantic?

6. At first, Kim was hesitant to return Bob's feelings. Where did she finally break down and admit to him that she did love him?

7. After they married, Kim discovered that she was pregnant. Why didn't she tell Bob?

8. During the course of their marriage, Bob and Kim were both the objects of psychotic obsessions. Doug Cummings stalked Kim, and later Laura Simmons became obsessed with Bob. How had Laura met Bob?

9. How did Laura insinuate herself into the Hughes home?

10. While Kim was caught up in dealing with Andy's alcoholism, a lonely Bob found comfort in the arms of another woman. Who was she?

As Irna Phillips Put It...

In 1957, Irna Phillips made the decision to kill off the character of Jim Lowell. Jim was sent off to Florida and died in a boating accident. The death did not sit well with the show's fans. Although Jim had been cheating on his wife, the audience sympathized with him and liked the character. Letters of complaint poured in to CBS, Procter & Gamble, and Phillips herself. Below, in code, is Phillips's reply to all those fans protesting Jim's surprise death.

To break the code, bear in mind that each letter stands for one and only other letter of the alphabet.

"MY VTK IXWEU VOWHY, IK RHXI VTK LEKMRHKYY

XQ IZHVKW, VTK FWXPZYK XQ YFWZHN, VTK

QOEEHKYY XQ YOPPKW, MHU VTKTMWGKYV XQ

MOVOPH....VTK JBJEK XQ EZQK ZY JX-

PFEKVK....ITMV ZY VWOK XQ VTK IXWEU,

HMVOWK, ZY MEYX VWOK XQ PMH. TK VXX TMY TZY

JBJEK."

The Reign of the Stewarts

After finally getting married, Ellen and David Stewart built one of *As the World Turns*'s core families during the late sixties and seventies. Paul was David's son from a previous marriage. Dan was Ellen's biological son, whom David and his late wife had adopted. Together, Ellen and David had two more children, daughters Dee and Annie. Although both Paul and Dan have died and Dee and Annie have left Oakdale, the Stewart clan lives on: Dan's daughter Emily is one of the show's leading vixens, and Dan's granddaughter Dani has been aged into her teens to fit into the show's youth story line.

1. What is Dee a nickname for?
   a. Dawn
   b. Deniece
   c. Diane
   d. Dorothy

2. What is Annie's first name?
   a. Anne
   b. Brigitte
   c. Carol
   d. Deborah

3. In the late sixties, Dan Stewart fell in love with Liz Talbot. He ended up getting both her and his wife Susan pregnant at the same time. What happened to the baby Susan was carrying?
   a. Susan had the child and named the girl Emily.
   b. The child died at birth.
   c. Susan miscarried.
   d. Susan had an abortion.

4. Also in love with Liz was Dan's brother Paul. Why did Liz marry him?
   a. simply to spite Dan
   b. to give her unborn child a name
   c. because she suspected that the baby was really Paul's
   d. because Susan blackmailed her into it

5. Why did Susan finally grant Dan a divorce?
   a. She had fallen in love with someone else herself.
   b. Ellen had offered her a large sum of money to set Dan free.
   c. Liz blackmailed her into it.
   d. Susan discovered that Liz was dying.

6. How long were Dan and Liz married before she died in a freak accident?
   a. a couple of days
   b. a month
   c. a year
   d. not at all—Liz died right before the wedding

7. How many children did Dan have?
   a. one
   b. two

   c. three

   d. four

8. How did Dan's brother Paul die?

   a. in a fire

   b. in a car accident

   c. suicide

   d. of a brain tumor

9. To whom was Dan married when he died?

   a. once again to Susan

   b. Kim Hughes

   c. Valerie Conway

   d. no one

10. Like their brothers Dan and Paul, Annie and Dee Stewart fell in love with the same person: law student Beau Spencer. Where had they met him?

   a. while on vacation in Europe

   b. through a personal ad

   c. in college

   d. He lived next door.

11. Although Annie ended up marrying Beau, he cheated on her with Melinda Gray. How did Melinda and Beau know each other?

   a. She was his secretary.

   b. He represented her in a divorce.

   c. She was a rival lawyer.

   d. She was his professor.

12. Melinda had some help breaking up Beau and Annie's marriage from Beau's mother Jane. What did Jane have against Annie?

   a. Annie had refused to let Jane live with Beau and her.

   b. Annie was encouraging Beau to pursue his dream of being a musician.

c. Annie was too independent.

d. Jane had long hated the Stewart family,

13. What did geologist Brad Hollister discover on property owned by the Stewart and Hughes families?
    a. gold
    b. silver
    c. oil
    d. uranium

14. Annie ended up marrying Brad, who had really wanted her sister Dee. When Annie learned the truth, she dumped Brad and wound up getting married to whom?
    a. Tom Hughes
    b. Steve Andropolous
    c. Craig Montgomery
    d. Jeff Ward

15. What was unusual about Annie's first pregnancy?
    a. She had been artificially inseminated.
    b. She had long been told that she couldn't have children.
    c. She was carrying quadruplets.
    d. It lasted eleven months.

16. After John Dixon was run down and left for dead, David Stewart mysteriously left town, making him the prime suspect in the investigation. Although David was not the hit-and-run driver, what motive did he have for wanting John dead?
    a. David held John responsible for Dan's death.
    b. John had gotten David fired from the hospital in order to take over his job.
    c. Dee had brought charges against John for marital rape.
    d. John had been blackmailing Ellen about her past.

17. Months after David's disappearance, Dee discovered him living in the town of Flat Rock and suffering from amnesia. David had made a new life for himself there, working as a pharmacist and engaged to Cynthia Haines, who owned the drugstore. How was David's memory restored?

   a. He was given sodium pentathol.

   b. He underwent hypnosis.

   c. He was hit by a car and woke up with his memory intact.

   d. His memory came back as soon as he returned to Oakdale.

18. Shortly after David returned to Oakdale, Ellen filed for divorce. What motivated her decision?

   a. Cynthia revealed that she was pregnant by David.

   b. Ellen herself had fallen in love with another man.

   c. Ellen discovered what she thought was proof that David had indeed tried to kill John.

   d. During David's absence, Ellen had grown to enjoy living on her own.

19. How did Lord Stewart Markham turn out to be David's grandson?

   a. David had had a son he never knew about, Stewart's father.

   b. David had had a daughter he never knew about, Stewart's mother.

   c. Stewart was Paul's son.

   d. Stewart was Dan's son.

20. Although Ellen and David had remarried shortly after their divorce, they spent the last few years of their marriage before David died living in different cities, sometimes different countries. What disease was David doing research on that kept him from coming back to Oakdale?

   a. AIDS

   b. breast cancer

c. cystic fibrosis

d. diabetes

Paging Dr. Dixon: Marriage to Kim

The friendship that currently exists between John Dixon and Kim Hughes belies a stormy history dating back to the early 1970s. At the time, Kim was in love with Bob, but he was married to her sister Jennifer. Kim allowed herself to be manipulated into a marriage to Bob's rival at the hospital, Dr. John Dixon. Although Kim did not love him, John was obsessed with her and managed to keep her tied to him for a number of years.

1. Why was John so obsessed with marrying Kim?
   a. He wanted to get even with her sister Jennifer, who had chosen Bob over him.
   b. Marriage to Kim would help him achieve the social status he'd been searching for.
   c. Kim was the spitting image of John's dead fiancée.
   d. John's father wanted him to marry Kim.

2. How did John use Kim's pregnancy to get him to marry her?
   a. He offered to give the baby a name.
   b. He reworked her pregnancy test to make it appear that he was the father.
   c. He threatened to expose Bob as the baby's father if Kim didn't marry him.
   d. He got close to Kim by treating her in private.

3. After Kim thought that the baby had died, she realized that she couldn't continue in her loveless marriage to John. John, in turn, resorted to blackmail to keep her from filing for divorce. Whom did he threaten to tell about Bob being the baby's father?
   a. Jennifer
   b. the hospital board
   c. Nancy and Chris
   d. Bob himself

4. John later learned that Kim's baby had not died at birth as she'd been led to believe, but had in fact been given to another couple. Why didn't John tell Kim the truth?
   a. He worried that it would bring her and Bob back together.
   b. He was bribed into keeping his mouth shut by the adoptive parents.
   c. He had heard that the baby was killed in a car accident and decided that it would only cause Kim unnecessary pain to know the whole truth.
   d. The doctors responsible for the switch threatened to implicate John if the truth came out.

5. Although John was worried about Kim's feelings for Bob, a new rival for her attention emerged in the form of Dan Stewart. Who opened John's eyes to Kim's feelings for Dan?
   a. Susan
   b. Dan's daughter Betsy
   c. Bob Hughes
   d. Jennifer Hughes

6. When Kim asked John for a divorce to marry Dan, how did John get Kim to reconsider her decision?
   a. He lied that Susan was pregnant.
   b. He lied that Susan was dying.
   c. He suggested that Susan, a recovering alcoholic, might fall off the wagon if Kim married Dan.
   d. He threatened to ruin Dan's medical career if Kim married him.

7. Kim left town to rethink her decision to marry Dan. Just as she decided that she would, she was caught in a natural disaster, during which she hit her head and developed amnesia. What sort of natural disaster brought about her amnesia?
   a. a landslide
   b. an earthquake

    c. a hurricane

    d. a tornado

8. While suffering from amnesia, Kim slept with John and conceived Andy. Kim then decided to stay with John for the sake of the baby. What did John do that finally pushed her to go through with getting a divorce?

    a. He slept with Susan Stewart.

    b. He manipulated a situation to get Bob Hughes fired from the hospital.

    c. He had Dan Stewart beaten up.

    d. He tried to force himself on Kim sexually.

9. Obsessed with raising Andy, John conspired to kidnap the boy. Which of his future wives helped him pull it off?

    a. Lucinda Walsh

    b. Pat Holland

    c. Dee Stewart

    d. Ariel Aldrin

10. Dan figured out that John was behind the kidnapping and managed to return Andy to Kim. How did John get even with Dan?

    a. He paid a patient to claim that Dan had made sexual advances to her.

    b. He convinced Susan to contest her divorce from Dan.

    c. He shot himself and blamed Dan.

    d. He cut the brake lines on Dan's car.

How Original

Viewers have had to adapt to seven Frannie Hugheses over the years, five Andy Dixons, and a dozen Tom Hugheses. Some roles, though, are so identified with the actor who played them that people forget someone else originated the role. Santos Ortega, for example, played Grandpa Hughes for twenty years (1956–76), but he did not play it from the very beginning. William Lee had the part for a total of three days before being replaced. Let's see how good you are at picking out which actors originated the roles they made famous. Draw a big "O" for "Original" next to the actors who created the roles they now play.

1. Helen Wagner (Nancy Hughes McCloskey)   _____
2. Patricia Bruder (Ellen Stewart)   _____
3. Don Hastings (Bob Hughes)   _____
4. Eileen Fulton (Lisa Grimaldi)   _____
5. Kathryn Hays (Kim Reynolds Hughes)   _____
6. Larry Bryggman (Dr. John Dixon)   _____
7. Marie Masters (Susan Stewart)   _____
8. Tom Wiggin (Kirk Anderson)   _____
9. Martha Byrne (Lily Walsh Grimaldi)   _____
10. Colleen Zenk Pinter (Barbara Ryan)   _____

Something Wicked This Way Comes

In the mid-1970s, as Lisa Mitchell was growing up and becoming less devious, the show needed a new villainess to shake things up around town. Filling that bill was Joyce Colman. Played by Barbara Rodell, Joyce was the wife of Lisa's lover Grant Colman and remained a thorn in their relationship for several years before moving on to spread her evil through the rest of Oakdale.

1. Why did Lisa accept Grant's marriage proposal even though he was still married to Joyce?
   a. because Grant believed that his divorce from Joyce was legal
   b. because Grant did not tell Lisa that he was married
   c. because Joyce was presumed dead
   d. because Joyce had been locked away in a mental institution

2. Although Joyce employed several different schemes to postpone legalizing her divorce from Grant, what legitimate medical emergency allowed her to delay the divorce yet again?
   a. an appendectomy
   b. temporary blindness
   c. a mild heart attack
   d. a hysterectomy

3. Even after Joyce finally consented to the divorce, she continued to drive a wedge between Grant and Lisa by telling Grant that she had given birth to his son three years previously and had given the baby up for adoption. When did Joyce reveal that news to Grant?
   a. as they were leaving the courthouse after being granted their divorce
   b. on Grant's wedding day to Lisa
   c. during his bachelor party
   d. at the funeral for Grant's mother

4. Mary and Brian Ellison had adopted Joyce and Grant's son, whom they named Teddy. Joyce eventually sued to regain custody of the boy. What did Grant do that so infuriated Joyce during the trial?
   a. He represented the Ellisons.
   b. He testified against Joyce's competence as a mother.
   c. He refused to remarry her.
   d. He discovered that he was not the baby's biological father and presented the evidence to the court.

5. What did Joyce do after losing the case?
   a. She kidnapped Teddy.
   b. She overdosed on sleeping pills and wine.
   c. She shot Grant.
   d. She went crazy and crashed her car.

6. Joyce went on to marry Donald Hughes, another of Lisa's ex-flames, whom she drove deeper and deeper into debt with her rampant spending. She also cheated on Donald with real estate agent Ralph Mitchell. Why did Ralph call off the affair?

a. He grew bored with Joyce.

b. He realized that Joyce was still hung up on Grant.

c. He fell in love with Kim.

d. He befriended Donald and felt guilty about sleeping with his new friend's wife.

7. Ralph not only broke up with Joyce, he insisted that she confess the affair to her husband. Joyce responded by plotting to kill Ralph. She planned to shoot him in her house and claim that she had mistaken him for a burglar. Instead, she shot Donald by accident. What happened to Donald as a result of that?

a. He died.

b. He was paralyzed from the waist down.

c. He went blind.

d. He lay in a coma for six months.

8. Who proved that the shooting was not an accident and that Joyce had intended to kill Ralph all along?

a. Grant

b. Lisa

c. Tom Hughes

d. Ralph himself

9. After Joyce's scheme was revealed, she fled town and was presumed dead. How had she supposedly died?

a. in a plane crash

b. in an explosion

c. in a car accident

d. by falling off a bridge

10. When Joyce returned from the presumed dead, she tried to win Grant back by claiming that she was dying from a brain tumor. Who exposed her scheme, prompting her to leave town, this time for good?
   a. Bob Hughes
   b. John Dixon
   c. Lisa
   d. Ralph Mitchell

The Widow Kim

By the time Kim Hughes arrived in Oakdale, she was already a widow. During her next ten years in town, she proceeded to bury another two husbands, Dan Stewart and Nick Andropolous.

   1. What was the name of Kim's first husband?
   a. Jason Reynolds
   b. Charles Eldridge
   c. David Conway
   d. Martin Guest

   2. Why did Kim's former sister-in-law Valerie Conway resent her so much?
   a. Kim controlled Valerie's trust fund.
   b. Kim had helped her late husband break up Valerie's relationship with an undesirable boyfriend.
   c. Valerie felt that she should have inherited the portion of the family estate that had gone to Kim.
   d. Valerie blamed Kim for her brother's death.

   3. What did Valerie do to get back at Kim?
   a. She caused a car accident that left Kim temporarily blind.
   b. She testified against Kim during Kim's custody battle with John Dixon.
   c. She kidnapped Andy when he was a baby.
   d. She dated Kim's estranged boyfriend Dan Stewart and lured him into an engagement.

4. After Kim and Dan married, what medical problem threatened their marriage?
  a. Kim discovered that she couldn't have any more children.
  b. Dan became impotent.
  c. A brain tumor made Dan subject to violent outbursts.
  d. Dan developed amnesia.

5. With whom did Dan have an affair while he was married to Kim?
  a. his ex-wife Susan
  b. Valerie Conway
  c. Lisa Miller
  d. Liz Talbot

6. A devious young woman named Melinda Gray came to live with Dan and Kim. Why did they take her in?
  a. Melinda said that Dan was her biological father.
  b. Melinda said that Kim's late husband was her biological father.
  c. Melinda said that Kim's late sister Jennifer was her biological mother.
  d. Melinda's father had died saving Dan's life in Vietnam.

7. Shortly after Kim forgave Dan for his affair and the two reconciled, Dan discovered that he was dying from what illness?
  a. liver cancer
  b. a brain tumor
  c. lupus
  d. kidney failure

8. Who fixed Kim up with restaurateur Nick Andropolous?
  a. Lisa Miller
  b. Nancy Hughes
  c. Dan's daughter Betsy
  d. Nick's brother Steve

9. What put Kim's plans to marry Nick on hold?
   a. Nick's presumed-dead wife turned out to be alive.
   b. Nick was arrested for smuggling jewelry.
   c. Nick was deported.
   d. Kim was kidnapped.

10. Kim eventually married Nick, who died of a heart attack shortly thereafter. What was it that triggered Nick's fatal heart attack?
    a. Kim revealed that she had slept with Bob Hughes the night before their wedding.
    b. James Stenbeck bankrupted Nick's restaurant.
    c. Nick discovered that his brother Steve had secretly been dating Betsy.
    d. Steve was arrested for selling drugs.

Oakdale and Points Beyond

Some of daytime's most popular actors have passed through Oakdale at one point in their careers. See if you can match up the following 12 actors and actresses with the roles they played on *As the World Turns*.

1. Linda Dano (Felicia Gallant, *Another World*)

   a. Kevin Thompson

2. Peter Simon (Ed Bauer, *Guiding Light*)

   b. Edith Hughes

3. Hillary B. Smith (Nora Gannon, *One Life to Live*)

   c. Eric Hollister

4. Michael Nader (Dimitri Marrick, *All My Children*)

   d. Debbie Simon

5. Leslie Charleson (Monica Quartermaine, *General Hospital*)

   e. Burke Donovan

6. Justin Deas (Buzz Cooper, *Guiding Light*)

   f. Cynthia Haines

7. Sharon Case (Sharon Collins,   **g.** Ian McFarland
   The Young and the Restless)
8. David Forsythe (John Hudson,   **h.** Andrea Korackas
   Another World)
9. Ruth Warrick (Phoebe Tyler   **i.** Brian McColl
   Wallingford, *All My Children*)
10. Mark Pinter (Grant Harrison,   **j.** Alice Whipple
    Another World)
11. Patricia Mauceri (Carlotta Vega,   **k.** Tom Hughes
    One Life to Live)
12. Peter Reckell (Bo Brady,   **l.** Margo Hughes
    Days of Our Lives)

Father's Day

Longtime characters Bob Hughes and John Dixon have each
fathered four children, some of whom they didn't even know
about until many years after the births. All you have to do is
name each doctor's four children, identify who each child's
mother is, and tell whether Bob or John was married to the
mother at the time the baby was conceived.

Bob Hughes   John Dixon

Child: _____   Child: _____

Mother: _____   Mother: _____

Married? _____   Married? _____

Child: _____   Child: _____

Mother: _____   Mother: _____

Married? _____   Married? _____

Child: _____   Child: _____

Mother: _____   Mother: _____

Married? _____   Married? _____

Child: _____   Child: _____

Mother: _____   Mother: _____

Married? _____   Married? _____

Satan's Younger Brother

Few villains can hold a candle to the devious James Stenbeck in terms of outright terror. No one could turn the town of Oakdale upside down quite the way he could. So on target was Anthony Herrera in the role that the writers brought James Stenbeck back from the dead again and again and again to unleash his terror on the decent and the not so decent citizens of Oakdale.

1. Under what circumstances did James Stenbeck first come to town?
   a. James owned a pharmaceutical company that was funding John Dixon's research on a revolutionary heart medication.
   b. The Stenbeck family plane crashed in a field outside town, and James had to be treated at Memorial Hospital.
   c. Geologist Brad Hollister brought James to town to refine the silver that was being mined on the Stewart family property.
   d. Lisa had met James during a trip to Europe and insisted that he come to the States with her.

2. James, it turned out, had been involved romantically years before with Barbara Ryan, who herself had only recently returned to town. Together they had had a son, Paul, whom the Stenbeck family pressured James into allowing another couple to raise. Why was James so eager to reunite with Barbara and raise their son together?
   a. A riding accident had left James incapable of fathering any more children.
   b. James wanted to get his hands on the money that Paul as a Stenbeck heir would inherit.
   c. Previous to coming to Oakdale, James wrongly believed himself sterile and thought that Paul had to be another man's son.
   d. James had been diagnosed with a terminal illness and thought that he was dying.

3. To whom was Barbara engaged when James wooed her back?
   a. Brian McColl
   b. Burke Donovan
   c. Tom Hughes
   d. John Dixon

4. With whom did James begin an affair shortly after marrying Barbara?
   a. Margo Montgomery
   b. Dee Stewart
   c. Annie Stewart
   d. Lisa Miller

5. What did James illegally traffic through Barbara and Lisa's boutique, Fashions Ltd.?
   a. fake passports
   b. government secrets
   c. cocaine
   d. leisure suits

6. How did James avoid prosecution for his part in that crime ring?
  a. He framed Steve Andropolous.
  b. He had diplomatic immunity.
  c. He paid off a police officer to "lose" the evidence against him.
  d. He turned state's evidence.

7. Why did Greta Aldrin discourage her daughter Ariel from pursuing a romance with James Stenbeck?
  a. Greta believed that James was possessed by the Devil.
  b. Greta was James's real mother, which made him Ariel's half brother.
  c. Greta wanted Ariel to go after the true Stenbeck heir.
  d. John Dixon, who wanted Ariel for himself, had paid Greta to keep Ariel away from James.

8. Why did James commit Barbara to an insane asylum?
  a. Barbara had learned the truth about his heritage.
  b. James needed to get control of Barbara's money.
  c. James wanted to better his chances for winning sole custody of Paul.
  d. James feared that Barbara was beginning to fall in love with the true Stenbeck heir.

9. In which of the following ways did James once try to kill Barbara?
  a. He walled her up in an alcove of the wine cellar at the Stenbeck family estate.
  b. He substituted a real gun for Paul's toy gun while Barbara and Paul were playing Cowboys and Indians.
  c. He dressed her in a red outfit and lured her into a bullfighting ring.
  d. He knocked her into the shark tank at the aquarium.

10. How did James Stenbeck "die" the first time he was presumed dead?
   a. He fell out of an airplane.
   b. His car exploded.
   c. His car went off the end of a pier.
   d. He was in a house that burned to the ground.

Separating the Actor From the Role

It's not uncommon for actors on any soap to receive mail addressed to their characters. Even when they go on talk shows and public appearances, audience members will refer to them by their characters' names. The following puzzle takes that confusion one step further, scrambling together actors' real names with their character names. All you have to do is unscramble each entry.

Sample

D M U N A O L G L H S H N E E L G E O R A
The actor's name: ELLEN DOLAN
The character's name: MARGO HUGHES

1. B L U H E H D B R U I D W L A B N A Z L A C H A E I T S

   The actor's name: _____

   The character's name: _____

2. O H S D H T B S E A G N U N B G H O S I

   The actor's name: _____

   The character's name: _____

3. R U M E Y N E T S T E W C A R N A L A Y

The actor's name: _____

The character's name: _____

4. T H S M H S M E O T H C G L U O E O T S

The actor's name: _____

The character's name: _____

5. N R C A N B E P L Z A Y A N N K E R E T B A I E O R R L

The actor's name: _____

The character's name: _____

6. H Y N L J R D R X A N B O N I G O R A M G Y

The actor's name: _____

The character's name: _____

7. M R H N K A S Y I S G H U T H A H E Y K

The actor's name: _____

The character's name: _____

8. K C K F R M H S T A S I N F I E H N W A A I S O N

The actor's name: _____

The character's name: _____

9. G L A E L K M S M W Y T E Y H I N E L A E R N E T I

The actor's name: _____

The character's name: _____

10. D G K W K N G R T I N A I S M N I R O E O

The actor's name: _____

The character's name: _____

True Love

While soap fans love to hear that their favorite couples have fallen in love in real life, backstage romances tend to be viewed as nightmares in the making by producers and writers. Always in the back of their minds are the nagging worries: What if this couple breaks up and doesn't want to work together anymore? What if the audience doesn't buy them as an on screen couple after they have broken up in real life? With or without the blessing of the higher-ups, though, *As the World Turns* has seen more than its share of backstage romances.

1. Which pair of actors who played Tom and Margo got married in real life as well?
   a. Justin Deas and Margaret Colin
   b. Justin Deas and Hillary Bailey Smith
   c. Hillary Bailey Smith and Gregg Marx
   d. Scott Holmes and Ellen Dolan

2. Which of the actresses who played Dee Stewart married Larry Bryggman, who played Dee's onscreen husband John Dixon?
   a. Marcia McClain
   b. Jacqueline Schultz
   c. Heather Cunningham
   d. Vicky Dawson

3. Colleen Zenk (Barbara Ryan) married Mark Pinter and added his name to her own. Which of Barbara's suitors did Pinter play on the show?
   a. Gunnar Stenbeck
   b. Brian McColl
   c. Darryl Crawford
   d. Franco Visconti

4. *Wings* star Steven Weber (Kevin Gibson) romanced Julianne Moore (Frannie Hughes) onscreen during his stint on *As the World Turns*. Which of the show's leading ladies, though, did he marry in real life?
   a. Jennifer Ashe (Meg Snyder)
   b. Mady Kaplan (Marie Kovac)
   c. Margaret Reed (Shannon O'Hara)
   d. Finn Carter (Sierra Estaban)

5. Which of the following popular couples got involved in real life and had to continue their onscreen romance after they had broken up?
   a. Lindsay Frost and Frank Runyeon (Betsy and Steve)
   b. Scott Bryce and Finn Carter (Craig and Sierra)
   c. Jon Hensley and Martha Byrne (Holden and Lily)
   d. Michael Swan and Margaret Reed (Duncan and Shannon)

6. As the promiscuous Julie Wendall, Susan Marie Snyder did love scenes opposite many of the show's leading men. Which one did she marry in real life?
   a. Scott DeFreitas (Andy Dixon)
   b. Peter Boynton (Tonio Reyes)
   c. Michael Louden (Duke Kramer)
   d. Graham Winton (Caleb Snyder)

7. While it is not uncommon for actors to fall in love while playing lovers, Jon Hensley (Holden Snyder) fell for which actress who played his sister on the show?
   a. Renee Props (Ellie)

    b. Jennifer Ashe (Meg)
    c. Lisa Brown (Iva)

8. Which of the following *As the World Turns* cast members did Marie Masters marry?
    a. John Reilly (Dan Stewart)
    b. Ed Fry (Larry McDermott)
    c. Robert Lipton (Jeff Ward)
    d. Larry Bryggman (John Dixon)

9. Kelley Menighan (Emily Stewart) recently married an actor who had played Emily's husband before Menighan took over the role. Who is he?
    a. Andy Kavovit (Paul Ryan)
    b. Anthony Herrera (James Stenbeck)
    c. Peter Boynton (Tonio Reyes)
    d. Jon Hensley (Holden Snyder)

10. Which of the current actors on the show met his current wife when she was brought on as a passing love interest for his character?
    a. Don Hastings (Bob Hughes)
    b. Tom Wiggin (Kirk Anderson)
    c. Scott Holmes (Tom Hughes)
    d. Patrick Tovatt (Cal Stricklyn)

Paging Dr. Dixon: The War With James Stenbeck

While John Dixon's rivalry with Bob Hughes and Dan Stewart had taken many nasty turns during the years, it was merely a warm-up for John's ongoing battle with James Stenbeck. On three separate occasions, James tried to kill John, and John had even gone so far as to fake his own murder in order to frame James Stenbeck for the crime.

1. How did James try to kill John the first time?

2. Why did James want John dead?

3. Although John survived the murder attempt, he did not escape completely unscathed. What happened to John as a result of James's murder attempt that left him unable to practice medicine?

4. James was prompted try to kill John a second time when John blackmailed James for $100,000, holding the truth about James's not being a true Stenbeck over his head. How had John learned that piece of information?

5. Which of John's wives had previously been married to James Stenbeck?

6. How were John and James once related by marriage?

7. John faked his own murder in order to frame James Stenbeck for the crime. The plan didn't work out quite the way John planned. Who wound up indicted for John's "murder"?

8. Where did John stage his "return from the dead"?

9. What sentence did John receive for faking his own murder?

10. After James himself "came back from the dead," he and John engaged in a near fatal battle on Lucinda Walsh's estate, during which James knocked John to the ground and was about to smash his head in with a large rock. Who successfully pleaded with James to spare John's life?

The Many Faces of Tom Hughes

The role of Tom Hughes is tied with *Search for Tomorrow*'s Patti Barron as the most recast role in soap opera history. From 1963, when James Madden first played Tom as a young boy, to the present day, a total of thirteen actors have been cast in the role. This quiz will determine how well you can tell one Tom from another.

1. Which actor has played Tom Hughes the longest?
   a. Scott Holmes
   b. Jason Kincaid
   c. Gregg Marx
   d. Justin Deas

2. Which 1970s prime-time TV star played Tom as a child in the mid 1960s?
   a. Henry Winkler from *Happy Days*
   b. David Soul from *Starsky and Hutch*
   c. Richard Thomas from *The Waltons*
   d. Ron Palillo from *Welcome Back Kotter*

3. How many of Justin Deas's five Emmy Awards were for playing Tom Hughes?
   a. zero
   b. one
   c. two
   d. three

4. What relationship is Gregg Marx, who played Tom in the mid 1980s, to the famous Groucho Marx?
   a. grandson
   b. great-nephew
   c. distant cousin
   d. no relation

5. Which former Tom Hughes told *Soap Opera Digest* that the character should have been killed off after he left the role?
   a. Jason Kinkead
   b. Gregg Marx
   c. Tom Tammi
   d. Justin Deas

Many a Margo

Although not recast as often as her husband Tom, the role of Margo (introduced in 1981) has been played by a total of four actresses: Margaret Colin, Hillary Bailey Smith, Ellen Dolan, and Glynnis O'Connor. (Ellen Dolan, the current Margo, left the role in 1993 and returned to it a year later.) In the following section are ten storyline highlights from Margo's fifteen-year history on the show. Beside each entry, write the initials of the actress who was playing Margo during that highlight. To make things a little more challenging, events have been jumbled chronologically.

1. Lost her hearing.   _____
2. Slept with Hal Munson.   _____
3. Discovered that John Dixon was her father.   _____
4. Gave birth to Adam in Greece.   _____
5. Was in a plane crash.   _____
6. Assisted in her stepfather Casey's right to die.   _____
7. Investigated the murder of Neal Alcott.   _____
8. Had an affair with James Stenbeck.   _____
9. Helped Tom break a cocaine ring led by Mr.   _____
   Big.
10. Was raped by an HIV-positive ex-convict.   _____

To Hollywood and Back

When an actor leaves a soap opera to go off to Hollywood and try to break into films, the reaction is almost always the same: *They'll be back.* Some, like Demi Moore, Alec Baldwin, and Kathleen Turner really have made it big. *As the World Turns* has sent a few of its alumni, like Meg Ryan, off to great success in Hollywood. But the show is not merely a stepping stone for future film actors. It has, in fact, given jobs to a number of actors who once lit up the silver screen. This quiz salutes the actors and actresses whose careers were launched by *As the World Turns* as well as those who have brought their Hollywood experience to daytime.

1. Ruth Warrick, an original cast member as Edith Hughes, made her film debut playing Orson Welles's wife in which of his films?
   a. *Macbeth*
   b. *Touch of Evil*
   c. *Citizen Kane*
   d. *The Trial*

2. Mark Rydell, who played Jeff Baker in the early 1960s, was nominated for an Oscar for directing what 1981 film?
   a. *Reds*
   b. *On Golden Pond*
   c. *Chariots of Fire*
   d. *Ordinary People*

3. Which current castmember costarred with Charlton Heston and Maximilian Schell in the World War II drama *Counterpoint*?
   a. Elizabeth Hubbard
   b. Kathryn Hays
   c. Eileen Fulton
   d. Kathleen Widdoes

4. In what capacity did child actor Freddie Bartholomew (*Little Lord Fauntleroy, Captains Courageous*) work on *As the World Turns*?
   a. headwriter
   b. music supervisor
   c. executive producer
   d. costume designer

5. Farley Granger, who played Lisa's sixth husband, Earl Mitchell, a spy, starred in two films directed by Alfred Hitchcock. Which two were they?

   a. *Shadow of a Doubt* and *Under Capricorn*
   b. *The Man Who Knew Too Much* and *Rear Window*
   c. *North by Northwest* and *Suspicion*
   d. *Strangers on a Train* and *Rope*

6. The 1966 Candice Bergen film *The Group* featured James Broderick, who had played Jim Norman during the early 1960s, as well as what future *As the World Turns* actress?

   a. Elizabeth Hubbard
   b. Kathryn Hays
   c. Kathleen Widdoes
   d. Marie Masters

7. James Earl Jones, who played Dr. Jerry Turner during the mid 1960s, provided the voice for which character in the *Star Wars* films?

   a. Yoda
   b. Jabba the Hut
   c. C3PO
   d. Darth Vader

8. Julianne Moore has made several films since leaving the dual role of Frannie and Sabrina. Which of the following is not one of her movies?

   a. *The Hand That Rocks the Cradle*
   b. *Assassins*
   c. *Nine Months*
   d. *Sabrina*

9. Which of the following *Wizard of Oz* stars appeared on *As the World Turns* in 1971?

   a. Margaret Hamilton (The Wicked Witch of the West)
   b. Ray Bolger (the Scarecrow)
   c. Bert Lahr (the Cowardly Lion)
   d. Billie Burke (Glinda the Good Witch)

10. Which actress went on to star in *The Joy Luck Club?*
    a. Parker Posey
    b. Jennifer Ashe
    c. Ming Na Wen
    d. Melanie Smith

11. Steven Weber (Kevin Gibson) played a character who was killed with a high-heeled shoe in what thriller?
    a. *Single White Female*
    b. *Seven*
    c. *Point of No Return*
    d. *Fatal Attraction*

12. Which actress, who has played Lily Walsh starred in the *Wilderness Family* movies as a child?
    a. Martha Byrne
    b. Lucy Deakins
    c. Heather Rattray

13. What *As the World Turns* alumna starred in the 1995 independent film *Party Girl?*
    a. Parker Posey
    b. Marisa Tomei
    c. Robin Morse
    d. Mary Ellen Stuart

14. Paolo Seganti (Damian Grimaldi) left *As the World Turns* in late 1995 to work in what film director's new project?
    a. Robert Redford
    b. Tim Burton
    c. Woody Allen
    d. Quentin Tarantino

15. What 1995 action film did Larry Bryggman (Dr. John Dixon) make while still starring *As the World Turns?*
    a. *Waterworld*
    b. *Batman Forever*

c. *Judge Dredd*

d. *Die Hard With a Vengeance*

To Hollywood and Back—The Sequel, Starring Meg Ryan

Unquestionably, the most successful star to emerge from *As the World Turns* has been Meg Ryan, who played the role of Betsy Stewart from 1982 to 1984. Since leaving the show, Ryan has made more than a dozen films and has become one of the highest-paid actresses in Hollywood.

1. Although Ryan found greatest success after leaving *As the World Turns*, she actually made her big-screen debut before coming on the show. In what 1981 film did she play Candice Bergen's daughter?
   a. *Mommie Dearest*
   b. *Rich and Famous*
   c. *Terms of Endearment*
   d. *On Golden Pond*

2. While on *As the World Turns*, Ryan appeared in the third entry of what horror film series?
   a. *The Amityville Horror*
   b. *A Nightmare on Elm Street*
   c. *Halloween*
   d. *Friday the 13th*

3. It was the 1986 box office smash *Top Gun* that sent Ryan's film career soaring. Although she got to kiss Tom Cruise, what current prime-time actor played her husband in the movie?
   a. Jimmy Smits from *NYPD Blue*
   b. Grant Show from *Melrose Place*
   c. Anthony Edwards from *ER*
   d. David Duchovny from *The X-Files*

4. Which of her leading men did Ryan marry in real life?
   a. Kevin Kline
   b. Val Kilmer
   c. Mark Harmon
   d. Dennis Quaid

5. In which Tom Hanks film did Ryan play three separate characters?
   a. *Splash*
   b. *Sleepless in Seattle*
   c. *Forest Gump*
   d. *Joe Versus the Volcano*

Paging Dr. Dixon: The Rape Trial

Inspired by the famous Rideout case, *As the World Turns* explored the issue of marital rape with John Dixon and his frigid young wife Dee. During a period of time in which the two were separated, John snuck back into their bedroom one night while Dee was sleeping and finally consummated their marriage. Dee in turn brought him up on rape charges. The trial was one of the most dramatic in the show's history.

1. What triggered Dee's fear of sex?

2. How did she become emotionally dependent upon John?

3. Whom did Dee truly love?

4. Dee's fear of sex forced her to reject the man she loved. What did he do that drove her into a surprising marriage to John Dixon?

5. What propelled Dee to throw John out?

6. Who represented Dee in her rape trial?

7. Who represented John in the case?

8. What secret did Lyla Montgomery reveal during her testimony on the witness stand?

9. What did Dee finally admit on the witness stand?

10. John got back at Dee and become rich at the same time by writing a book about the trial. What was the book titled?

Oakdale's Answer to Luke and Laura

The phenomenal success of Luke and Laura's romance on *General Hospital* in the early eighties gave rise to a number of similar good-girl/bad-boy love stories all across daytime. Fitting the bill of bad boy on *As the World Turns* was the short-tempered Steve Andropolous, played by Frank Runyeon. Not only had Steve slept with his older brother Nick's wife, he and his sister-in-law had been partners in a jewelry heist as well. Betsy Stewart (played by Meg Ryan, later by Lindsay Frost), who herself was a little rebellious in her teens, seemed to be attracted to less than noble men. She married Craig Montgomery, who at the time was an unscrupulous corporate climber; and after her marriage to Steve broke up, she got involved with one-time rapist Josh Snyder. Although Steve and Betsy were the show's supercouple in the early eighties, their marriage and love story ended on a low note in 1986 when Steve returned to a life of crime and went to prison in his homeland of Greece.

1. How was Steve Betsy's "uncle" when they started dating?
   a. For immigration reasons, Steve was faking a marriage to Betsy's aunt, Dee Stewart.
   b. For immigration purposes, Betsy's grandfather David Stewart had adopted Steve.
   c. His brother Nick was married to Betsy's stepmother, Kim.
   d. Steve's biological father had once been married to Betsy's biological mother, Elizabeth.

2. Nick did not take the news well when he learned about Steve and Betsy. How did hearing of their involvement lead to his death?

a. His shock and anger triggered a massive heart attack.

b. He got into a fight with Steve, during which Nick fell down a flight of stairs and broke his neck.

c. Nick got drunk and was killed driving home.

d. Thinking his family honor disgraced, he committed suicide.

3. Feeling responsible for Nick's death, Betsy broke up with Steve and jumped into marriage with Craig Montgomery. Why was Craig so eager to marry Betsy?

a. He needed a respectable wife to move ahead at work.

b. Ellen Stewart had offered him money to keep Betsy away from Steve.

c. Craig wanted to get his hands on Betsy's trust fund.

d. Craig and Steve had been bitter rivals since childhood.

4. While still married to Craig, Betsy got pregnant by Steve. How did Betsy's grandfather David Stewart know that Craig was not the father?

a. Betsy's amniocentesis revealed a genetic condition prevalent in Steve's family.

b. David knew that Craig was sterile.

c. David had performed a vasectomy on Craig.

d. David was treating Craig for impotence.

5. After whom did Betsy name her and Steve's daughter?

a. her grandmother Ellen

b. her stepmother, Kim

c. her biological mother, Elizabeth

d. her father, Dan

6. Once Steve and Betsy extricated themselves from their unhappy marriages, they got back together. Where did Steve propose to Betsy?
   a. on the beach
   b. on the roof of the Stewart cabin
   c. at a construction site
   d. in the college library

7. During what sweeps month did Steve and Betsy get married?
   a. February
   b. May
   c. November

8. Meg Ryan left the show shortly after Steve's marriage to Betsy, and Lindsay Frost took over the role. To explain the change, the writers put a bizarre twist on the old plastic surgery gimmick. A disturbed doctor named Russ Elliot had Betsy turned into the spitting image of his late wife. Why had Russ felt responsible for his wife's death?
   a. She had died in a car accident while he was driving.
   b. He had misdiagnosed her illness.
   c. She had been killed by his mistress.
   d. She committed suicide over his affair.

9. How did Russ try to kill Steve while Steve was in the hospital being treated for hepatitis?
   a. He poisoned Steve's IV bag.
   b. He turned off Steve's oxygen.
   c. He switched Steve's ID bracelet with that of a patient undergoing risky heart surgery.
   d. He changed the medicine dosage on Steve's chart.

10. After Lucinda Walsh drove his construction company into ruin, Steve returned to a life of crime and was ultimately imprisoned in Greece. What was he smuggling into the country when he got arrested?
   a. stolen artwork
   b. stolen jewelry
   c. illegal firearms
   d. drugs

Kim's Secret Admirer

Often hailed as one of the best mysteries spun out on daytime, the Doug Cummings story started shortly after Kim and Bob returned home from their honeymoon. Kim, a former singer, began receiving gifts, phone calls, and song lyrics from a secret admirer. Several people were suspected of sending the gifts, including her former husband John Dixon and her former accompanist Ken Wayne. The real culprit turned out to be Doug Cummings, a new restaurant owner in town who had been obsessed with Kim since his youth, when he used to listen to her sing. In his twisted quest to become part of Kim's family, he left a string of dead bodies along the way. After he was killed by his equally psychotic and obsessive assistant Marsha Talbot, Kim stood trial for the murder.

1. Which of the following was not a gift Doug had sent to Kim?
   a. apricot roses
   b. a locket with an old publicity photo of herself inside
   c. a kitten
   d. an antique key

2. From what standard did the song lyrics come that Doug sent to Kim?
   a. "Unforgettable"
   b. "You Made Me Love You"
   c. "Someone to Watch Over Me"
   d. "I'll Be Seeing You"

3. How did Doug insinuate himself into the Hughes family?
   a. He rented the apartment over Bob and Kim's garage.
   b. He dated Frannie.
   c. He claimed to be a distant cousin.
   d. He befriended Tom Hughes.

4. With what was Marie Kovac strangled to death?
   a. black ribbon
   b. a man's necktie
   c. a woman's scarf
   d. piano wire

5. What evidence proving that Doug was Kim's admirer did Frannie and Kim discover in his apartment, prompting him to take them both hostage?
   a. a love letter he had written to Kim
   b. Bob and Kim's wedding photo with Doug's face superimposed over Bob's
   c. Kim's missing wedding ring
   d. Doug's secret shrine to Kim

6. What was the name of the Colorado millhouse where Doug was born and where he took Kim and Frannie hostage?
   a. Avalon
   b. Briarwood
   c. Cumming's Manor
   d. Dream's End

7. After Bob heard that Kim and Frannie had been kidnapped, he also discovered that Kim was pregnant. Who filled him in?
   a. his mother, Nancy
   b. Kim's obstetrician
   c. Lisa
   d. John Dixon

8. While Doug was trying to rape Frannie, how did Marsha Talbot kill him?
   a. She stabbed him.
   b. She shot him.
   c. She hit him over the head with a blunt object.
   d. She pushed him out a window.

9. Thinking that Frannie had killed Doug, Kim took the blame for the murder. Why didn't Frannie tell Kim she was innocent?
   a. Frannie was catatonic after the murder.
   b. Frannie couldn't remember anything that happened after Doug tried to rape her.
   c. Marsha Talbot threatened to have Frannie's entire family killed if Frannie talked.
   d. Frannie blamed Kim for everything that happened and wanted to see her punished.

10. In his will, to whom did Doug Cummings leave his entire estate?
   a. Kim
   b. Frannie
   c. Marsha
   d. Kim's unborn child, which he believed was his

Hand-Me-Down Lovers

When Lien Hughes arrived in Oakdale, she began dating Paul Ryan, then moved on to his cousin Andy Dixon, whom she left for his half brother Duke. Lien was far from the first or the last person in Oakdale to romance two or more members from the same family.

1. Who slept with Lucinda Walsh and both of her half sisters, Neal Alcott and Samantha Markham, neither of whom he realized at the time was Lucinda's sister?

2. Which two pairs of brothers did Julie Wendall sleep with?

3. Who got pregnant by Dan Stewart and then married his brother Paul?

4. On which of her seven husbands did Lisa Miller cheat with his own brother?

5. Which of her ex-brothers-in-law did Lisa try to corral into marriage?

6. Who slept with Lucinda, her daughter Sierra, and her (Lucinda's) half sister Samantha?

7. What two leading men have slept with both Lily's biological mother, Iva, and her adoptive mother, Lucinda?

8. Who slept with James Stenbeck as well as his son, Paul Ryan?

9. What pair of sisters fell in love with geologist Brad Hollister?

10. Which leading man got two sisters pregnant at the same time?

Square Dancing by the Snyder Pond

While it is not uncommon for lovers to move from one family member to the next in Oakdale, it did seem to happen a bit more than usual down around the Snyder farm. Maybe with all the square dancing they do in their barn, changing partners comes a bit too easily to the Snyders.

1. Who courted Emma Snyder, then got involved with her daughter Iva?

2. Which two leading men have been involved with both Ellie and Iva Snyder?

3. What three women have been involved with both Holden and Caleb Snyder?

4. Which of those three women went on to marry Holden and Caleb's older brother Seth?

5. Which Snyder brother mistook Sabrina Fullerton for her look-alike sister/cousin Frannie and made love to her by mistake?

James Stenbeck, Back From Hell

As fate would have it, James Stenbeck had a parachute with him when he fell out of that airplane in 1983. He returned to Oakdale three years later to continue his reign of terror and to claim his son Paul. During his return visit from hell, James "died" another couple of times before doing it for real in 1989.

1. Barbara was the first person to meet James in the catacombs underneath Duncan McKechnie's castle. How was James dressed when Barbara first came across him?
   a. in surgical scrubs
   b. in a monk's robe
   c. in a tuxedo
   d. in nothing at all

2. As a favor to Barbara, Lucinda Walsh hired James to work at Walsh Enterprises so that she could keep an eye on him. What exactly did Lucinda hire James to do for her?
   a. spy on the competition
   b. run security
   c. collect on outstanding loans
   d. consult on the foreign market

3. Why did Lucinda ultimately fire him?
   a. He had tried to take over the company.
   b. He was using the company jet to transport drugs.
   c. He tried to seduce her daughter Sierra.
   d. The stockholders objected to him working there.

4. While in Oakdale, James carried on simultaneous affairs with a number of different women. Which of the following was not one of them?
   a. Emily Stewart
   b. Meg Snyder
   c. Lucinda Walsh
   d. Corinne Lawrence

5. When Lucinda refused to help James steal his son Paul away from Barbara, he kidnapped Lucinda's daughter Lily to make Lucinda cooperate. Who rescued Lily and got shot in the process?
   a. her father, Josh
   b. Holden Snyder
   c. Dusty Donovan
   d. Lucinda herself

6. A bullet-riddled corpse was found at one of Lucinda's spare homes in Ruxton Hills. Although burned beyond recognition, the body was identified as that of James Stenbeck. A number of people wanted him dead, but who was convicted for James's murder and went to prison?
   a. Lucinda Walsh
   b. Barbara Ryan
   c. Tonio Reyes
   d. John Dixon

7. As it turned out, James Stenbeck was still alive. The body the police discovered belonged to Nick Castello, a crooked cop on James's payroll. How had James arranged for Nick's body to be mistaken for his own?
   a. James substituted Nick's fingerprints for his own in the police records.
   b. James drained Nick's body of blood and transfused in a pint of his own.
   c. James cut off his own hand and left it beside Nick's body.

d. James had made Nick undergo dental work identical to his own.

8. James was declared dead for a third time down by the docks in New York City during the fall of 1989. How had he presumedly been killed this time around?
   a. James was shot by the police several times and fell off the end of the pier.
   b. His boat exploded.
   c. His helicopter was shot down over the bay.
   d. James was harpooned by Barbara and fell over the side of his boat.

9. James returned to Oakdale one final time to claim his mistress Emily and his son Paul. When he discovered that Emily had slept with Paul, it triggered a murderous rage. How did James learn about Emily and Paul?
   a. Barbara told him.
   b. He found a letter Paul had written to Emily.
   c. James had secretly installed video cameras in Emily's apartment.
   d. He overheard Paul talking about it with Andy Dixon.

10. How did Paul end up killing James in order to save Emily's life?
    a. He shot him.
    b. He stabbed him.
    c. He hit him over the head with a candlestick.
    d. He pushed him out a window.

The Prime-Time Exchange Program

While there remains a prejudice among producers of prime-time shows against hiring soap actors, a few manage to sneak though every now and again. Balancing things out, a number of prime-time stars have also made their way onto daytime over the years.

1. Which current cast member became a teen idol playing the Video Ranger on the 1950s science fiction series *Captain Video*?
   a. Don Hastings
   b. Larry Bryggman
   c. Patrick Tovatt
   d. Simon Prebble

2. John Wesley Shipp, who terrorized the Hughes family as archvillain Doug Cummings in the mid eighties, played what comic book hero in a late eighties TV series of the same name?
   a. Superboy
   b. Spiderman
   c. Captain America
   d. The Flash

3. David McCallum (Vermeil) and Robert Vaughn (Rick Hamilton) had short-term roles on *As the World Turns* at different times during the last fifteen years. On what popular spy series had they starred together back in the 1960s?
   a. *I Spy*
   b. *Mission Impossible*
   c. *The Man from U.N.C.L.E.*
   d. *The Avengers*

4. On what 1960s supernatural sitcom did Lisa Loring (Cricket Montgomery) play a girl named Wednesday?
   a. *The Addams Family*
   b. *Bewitched*
   c. *The Munsters*
   d. *The Ghost and Mrs. Muir*

5. Danny Pintauro, who created the role of Paul Stenbeck as a boy, left the show to star on what long-running ABC sitcom?
   a. *Full House*
   b. *Growing Pains*

   c. *Family Matters*
   d. *Who's the Boss?*

6. Which of Frannie Hughes's boyfriends did *Wings* star Steven Weber play?
   a. Seth Snyder
   b. Sean Baxter
   c. Kevin Gibson
   d. Larry McDermott

7. Which sister on *Sisters* played Ellie Bradley in 1971?
   a. Sela Ward
   b. Swoozie Kurtz
   c. Julianne Phillips
   d. Patricia Kalember

8. On what police drama had Dan Frazer played a police officer before taking on the role of police lieutenant Dan McCloskey?
   a. *Hill Street Blues*
   b. *Police Woman*
   c. *Kojak*
   d. *Police Story*

9. Between his roles as Kevin Thompson on *As the World Turns* and Dimitri Marrick on *All My Children*, Michael Nader played Dex Dexter on what prime-time soap opera?
   a. *Dallas*
   b. *Dynasty*
   c. *Knots Landing*
   d. *Falcon Crest*

10. For what prime-time series did alumna Dana Delaney (Hayley Wilson) win an Emmy award?
   a. *China Beach*
   b. *St. Elsewhere*
   c. *ER*
   d. *Hill Street Blues*

Lisa Miller Hughes, et cetera: A Woman of Mystery

Michael Shea was the first but far from the last of Lisa's husbands to be murdered. At last body count, the Widow Grimaldi had buried a total of four husbands, all of them murder victims. Lisa herself, it should be noted, has been kidnapped and targeted for murder a number of times during her life.

1. While Lisa was running the Wade Bookshop, a number of attempts were made on her life. Although many people suspected the moody young Jay Stallings, who lived next to the store, the culprit turned out to be Jay's stepfather Gil Stallings. Gil was trying to frame Jay for murder to get control of Jay's inheritance. Which of Lisa's future husband's rescued her and Jay from his evil stepfather?
   a. Earl Mitchell
   b. Whit McColl
   c. Grant Colman
   d. Donald Hughes

2. Why was Bennett Hadley obsessed with Lisa from the first moment he met her?
   a. He had followed her career as a torch singer.
   b. He mistakenly believed that she was his mother.
   c. She was the spitting image of his dead wife.
   d. He had seen her in psychic visions.

3. Lisa's fifth husband, Whit McColl, was killed by Dorothy Connors. In what capacity had Dorothy worked for Whit?
   a. horse trainer
   b. housekeeper
   c. secretary
   d. private investigator

4. What secret about Dorothy was revealed after Whit's murder?
   a. that she had secretly been married to Whit for years
   b. that she was the mother of his son Kirk

c. that she was his half sister

d. that she was really a man

5. Lisa had suspected that Lucinda Walsh may have killed her husband. What motive did Lucinda have for wanting Whit McColl dead?

   a. He was blackmailing her.

   b. He was going to sue for custody of Lily, who was his biological daughter.

   c. He was trying to take over her company.

   d. She believed that he had driven her husband, Martin Guest, to suicide.

6. What was the dangerous occupation of Husband Number 6, Earl Mitchell?

   a. police detective

   b. bounty hunter

   c. Interpol agent

   d. private investigator

7. What criminal mastermind instructed Glenn Harrington to kill Earl Mitchell?

   a. Tonio Reyes

   b. Gavin Kruger

   c. Mr. Big

   d. James Stenbeck

8. After killing Earl, Glenn and an Earl Mitchell look-alike made Lisa believe that Earl was still alive. When she realized that she had been fooled, which ex-husband did she suspect might be behind the charade?

   a. Grant Colman

   b. Bennett Hadley

   c. John Eldridge

   d. Bob Hughes

9. How did Glenn try to kill Lisa so that it would look like a suicide?
   a. He tried to hang her.
   b. He sealed up all the doors and windows and turned on the gas oven.
   c. He forced her to swallow a mouthful of sleeping pills.
   d. He tried to throw her off her own balcony.

10. After being shot by Hans the terrorist, Eduardo Grimaldi, Lisa's seventh husband, was rushed to the hospital, where Orlena Grimaldi finished him off. What secret was Orlena afraid Eduardo would reveal?
    a. that Damian was not really her son
    b. that Damian was really his son from their brief affair
    c. that Orlena had killed her husband, Damian's father
    d. that Damian's son, Luciano, was really Holden Snyder's son

No Family Resemblance Whatsoever

It's not unusual for actors to play more than one role on a soap opera. The medium is filled with long-lost twins, evil impostors, and split personalities. The following dual roles, however, are noteworthy because they fall into none of these categories. The second roles these actors came back to play were never conceived of as look-alikes to the actors' previous roles. In one or two cases, any hint of a resemblance between the roles borders on the downright creepy.

1. There was a span of almost thirty years between Nicholas Coster's stints on *As the World Turns*. During both runs, he not only got to romance Lisa Miller, he actually married her. Which two of Lisa's seven husbands did Coster play? (He played one of the roles on both *As the World Turns* and its prime-time spin-off, *Our Private World*.)

2. From 1972 to 1973, Ariane Munker played Annie Stewart. Five years later, she returned to the show as another character who ended up stealing away Annie's husband Beau Spencer. What was the name of the second character Ariane Munker played?

3. As the villainous James Stenbeck, Anthony Herrera has made numerous return visits to Oakdale throughout much of the 1980s. Five years before he made his debut as James Stenbeck, who bedded Emily Stewart, he appeared on the show as a potential love interest for Emily's mother, Susan Stewart. What was the character's name?

4. What actress played John Dixon's future wife Dee Stewart as a child and his daughter Margo Hughes as an adult?

5. Leslie Denniston met her future husband Don Hastings (Bob Hughes) while playing the role of Karen Peters, a passing love interest for Bob in the late 1970s. The contact between Denniston and Hastings was even more passing when she returned to the show in the early 1990s. What murder victim did she play at that time?

A.K.A.

For amnesiacs and criminal masterminds, a spare identity is more than a luxury; it's a tool of survival. The following quiz reveals the varied aliases different characters have assumed to elude the police, plot corporate takeovers, and write romance novels.

1. Lucinda Walsh changed her name because she wanted to distance herself from her poor background and reinvent herself as someone glamorous. What name had she been born with?

2. By what code name was druglord Bernard Grayson better known?

3. Which criminal mastermind had committed murder under the alias Lester Keyes and was known by the code name The Falcon?

4. By what other name was Lily Walsh's biological father, Josh Snyder known when he showed up in Oakdale?

5. Which character went by the name Donald Saunders while suffering from amnesia?

6. After Holden Snyder lost his memory, he chose the name Aaron for himself. What significance did the name Aaron have for Holden that he couldn't remember?

7. In the early 1960s, what character played piano under the stage name Jack Bailey?

8. How did Erin Casey come up with the name Shannon O'Hara when she came to the United States?

9. Under what pen name did Emma Snyder write a romance novel?

10. What name has Umberto Calderon used to insinuate himself into Lily Grimaldi's life?

Name Droppers

While changing one's name is not as prevalent in show business as it used to be, some performers, like the five actresses mentioned here, have chosen to change a first name or a last name or both.

1. What name was Eileen Fulton born with?
   a. Catherine Tately
   b. Constance Hunt
   c. Eunice Cuff
   d. Margaret McLarty

2. What is Martha Byrne's real first name?
   a. Elizabeth
   b. Patricia
   c. Mary
   d. Gayle

3. Like Martha Byrne, Renee Props (who played Ellie Snyder) also goes by her middle name. What is her real first name?
   a. Alicia
   b. Babette
   c. Courtney
   d. Drucilla

4. Where did Kathryn Hays (who was born Kathryn Piper) find the last name Hays?
   a. She read the name Kathryn Hays in a novel and liked the way it sounded.
   b. It was her mother's maiden name.
   c. She named herself after Helen Hayes.
   d. She named herself after Isaac Hayes.

5. Which current actress on the show was born Marie Mastruserio?
   (Sorry, but this one's too easy for a multiple choice.)

John and Lucinda's Love/Hate/Love Affair

John Dixon and Lucinda Walsh's elopement surprised most of Oakdale—including John and Lucinda themselves. John's proposal of marriage came during the middle of one of their many heated arguments. When Lucinda Walsh first arrived in town, she and John had been seeing each other, but their relationship took a bad turn and they became the most bitter of enemies. Lucinda stole John's seat on the hospital board, and John retaliated by blackmailing Lucinda about Sierra Estaban being her daughter and Lily not being her daughter. Marriage put an end to John's blackmail and gave him a rare opportunity to be on the receiving end of spousal manipulation.

1. How had John and Lucinda met in Chicago before coming to Oakdale?
   a. John had been her mother's doctor.
   b. They had gone to medical school together.
   c. John had dated Lucinda's sister.
   d. Lucinda's first husband had been John's first boss.

2. What did Lucinda do that turned her budding relationship with John into a bitter rivalry?
   a. Her foundation cut off funding for his medical research.
   b. She voted for Bob Hughes to be head of the hospital.
   c. She slept with his archenemy James Stenbeck.
   d. Her paper published a story that John had told her in confidence.

3. Which of the following was not one of the demands John made of Lucinda in exchange for his keeping silent about her being Sierra's mother?
   a. that she give up her hospital board seat to him
   b. that she convince Sierra to become his assistant
   c. that her newspaper run an exposé slandering Bob Hughes
   d. that she stop Craig and Sierra's wedding

4. How did John discover that Lily was not Lucinda's biological daughter?
   a. When Lily needed a blood transfusion, he cross-matched her type with Lucinda's.
   b. He caught Lucinda trying to doctor Lily's medical records.
   c. Iva Snyder confided the truth to him.
   d. After a car accident, Lucinda mumbled the truth in her delirium.

5. During a heated argument about her newspaper harassing Andy, what broke the tension between John and Lucinda and prompted him to propose marriage?
   a. Spooked by John's yelling, the horse Lucinda was riding threw her.
   b. Lucinda pushed John into her bathtub, and he pulled her in after him.
   c. Lucinda experienced an angina attack.
   d. The pilot announced that the plane they were on was about to crash.

6. To where did John and Lucinda elope?
   a. Paris
   b. Mexico City
   c. Las Vegas
   d. Acapulco

7. John walked out on Lucinda when he discovered that she had tried to manipulate his newly discovered son Duke Kramer into leaving town. How did Lucinda try to send Duke back to Seattle?
   a. She offered him $100,000 to open his own gym there.
   b. She convinced Duke that his presence in town was going to push his alcoholic brother Andy off the wagon.
   c. She hired Duke's ex-girlfriend Julie Wendall to lure him back to Seattle.
   d. She planted cocaine in his locker at the gym.

8. With whom did John have an affair while separated from Lucinda?
   a. Emma Snyder
   b. Kim Hughes
   c. Iva Snyder
   d. Susan Stewart

9. Which of John's sons did Lucinda legally adopt?
   a. Andy Dixon
   b. Dusty Donovan

   c. Duke Kramer

   d. Iva Snyder's unborn child

10. What was the final straw that pushed John into divorcing Lucinda?

   a. She bankrupted the Snyder farm.

   b. She hid evidence that Duke Kramer was really John's son.

   c. She slept with Cal Stricklyn.

   d. She ruined John's chances of being offered a prestigious job in another city.

An Honor Just to Be Nominated

An Emmy was first presented to a soap opera in 1972 when *The Doctors* was given the award for Outstanding Achievement in Daytime Drama. It would be another fourteen years, though, before *As the World Turns* would even be nominated as Outstanding Series. It would take almost as long before any of the show's actors would be recognized for their work.

1. How many times has *As the World Turns* been named Outstanding Daytime Drama Series?

2. In 1984, Brian Bloom (who played Dusty Donovan) became the first actor to win the Emmy in what newly created category?

3. In 1984, Larry Bryggman won his first Emmy as Outstanding Actor. Which of his castmates was also nominated that year for the very same award?

4. How many daytime Emmys has Larry Bryggman won for his portrayal of John Dixon?

5. Who is the only actor or actress to pick up an Emmy award for playing a dual role on the show?

6. In what category was Gillian Spencer (who had created the role of Jennifer Ryan Hughes in the early 1970s) nominated for her work on *As the World Turns?*

7. Which actor won the Emmy as Best Supporting Actor in 1986 after his character had been killed off?

8. Which role has earned Emmy awards for two of the actors who played it?

9. Who is the only actress currently on *As the World Turns* to have won an Emmy award for her work on the show?

10. Which three of *As the World Turns's* former head writers have been awarded Trustees Awards for Continued Service to Daytime?

Worth Quoting

"I love you." "You're not going anywhere till I get the truth." "What do you mean you slept with her?" Almost every character in Oakdale has uttered these lines at one time or another, usually several times during the course of a year. Then there are those lines that only a certain character could get away with. Who else but Susan Stewart, while being pressured into having a baby, would dare say to John Dixon, even in jest, "You're pretty densely populated. Why don't you give us one of yours?" And who else but the status-conscious Edwina Walsh Cabot would have thought up an insult like "You have the breeding of kitchen help." As these examples and many of the quotes used in the quiz below illustrate, the most memorable lines do tend to be the ones that make us laugh.

1. Which menopausal heroine once shot down any talk of starting a new romance with the line "I'm having hot flashes. I don't need a broken heart."
   a. Kim Hughes
   b. Lucinda Walsh

    c. Lisa Mitchell

    d. Emma Snyder

2. About which prospective son-in-law was Susan Stewart talking when she said, "Just what I always wanted for my daughter—a husband who brings his psychiatrist to the wedding."

    a. Royce Keller

    b. Holden Snyder

    c. Paul Ryan

    d. James Stenbeck

3. Upon spying which corporate executive in a tight-fitting dress did Kirk Anderson once quip, "Kind of tough to hide your battle-ax in that outfit, isn't it?"

    a. Lucinda Walsh

    b. Emily Stewart

    c. Connor Walsh

    d. Evan Walsh

4. About whom was John Dixon talking when he said, "Don't tell me about your son's trip to the fertility factory. It's going to take more than microsurgery to make a man out of him."

    a. Andy Dixon

    b. Bob Hughes

    c. Craig Montgomery

    d. Dan Stewart

5. Which family member told Lucinda off in the following fashion: "You cannot buy me. You cannot control me. And you sure as hell cannot outsmart me."

    a. her half sister Samantha

    b. her half brother Royce

    c. her stepson Duke

    d. her son-in-law Holden

6. Where was Emma Snyder when she made the observation "It's impossible to have a private conversation here without everyone popping in and out."
   a. Julie Wendall's bedroom
   b. the ladies' room at the Mona Lisa
   c. Lucinda Walsh's office
   d. the Snyder family kitchen

7. To whom did Emily Stewart say the following: "Everyone knows you're truth-impaired. It's a disability. It happens."
   a. her mother, Susan
   b. Lucinda Walsh
   c. Kirk Anderson
   d. Barbara Ryan

8. About whom was Margo Hughes talking when she said the following to her mother-in-law, Lisa Grimaldi: "You don't need a jury to hang this man. You've already done it all by yourself."
   a. her father, John Dixon, whom Lisa was suing for malpractice
   b. her brother Craig Montgomery, whom Lisa suspected of killing her fifth husband, Whit McColl
   c. her partner Hal Munson, whom Lisa was suing for false arrest
   d. her brother Andy, who had collided with Lisa's car while he was driving drunk

9. Which leading man said the following to his romantic rival: "Anyone who helped bring my son into the world should be my friend for life, but you are not my friend."
   a. Steve Andropolous to Craig Montgomery
   b. Hal Munson to Tom Hughes
   c. John Dixon to Bob Hughes
   d. Damian Grimaldi to Holden Snyder

10. After being jilted at the altar, which troubled heroine vowed the following: "I'm going to write 1993 off as one long, bad hair day."
    a. Lily Walsh
    b. Julie Wendall
    c. Emily Stewart
    d. Rosanna Cabot

From Lucinda's Own Lips

Lucinda Walsh doesn't care what too many people in Oakdale think of her, and she is rarely hesitant to speak her mind. As a result, many of *As the World Turns*'s funniest comebacks and observations have fallen from her lips.

1. Whom was John Dixon considering inviting to dinner, prompting Lucinda to remark, "Is that a date or a controlled experiment?"

2. To what situation was Lucinda referring when she said, "Trust Emily to figure out a way to have a baby without losing her figure."

3. Which of Oakdale's leading men did Lucinda one time describe as "that grimly attractive detective"?

4. With which of her employee ex-lovers did Lucinda have the following exchange: "You're all out of tricks, Lucinda." "I still have you."

5. Which character did she once refer to as "the town oddity"?

The Haunting of McKechnie Castle

Duncan McKechnie brought more than a touch of Gothic suspense to Oakdale when he arrived in the mid 1980s. A descendant of pirates, Duncan showed up in town with a disturbed "sister" named Beatrice, who was later revealed to be his daughter. His never-before-mentioned wife Lilith showed up a few years after that having been released from a sanatarium in Europe. The McKechnie family castle, which had been shipped over from Scotland stone by stone, was literally haunted, and dead bodies were constantly being unearthed on the island he had bought off the coast of Oakdale. None of those things, as bizarre as they were, could have prepared him for how his marriage to Shannon O'Hara would come to an end.

1. Shannon had married Duncan while in a drunken stupor, but Shannon never bothered filing for divorce because she believed that he had been killed in what sort of natural disaster?
   a. avalanche
   b. tidal wave
   c. cave-in
   d. rock slide

2. When did Duncan choose to reveal to Shannon that he was still alive?
   a. the night before she was to marry John Dixon
   b. during her wedding to Brian McColl
   c. on the tenth anniversary of their wedding
   d. the day before he was to be declared legally dead

3. What had a fortune-teller told Beatrice and Brian McColl regarding their upcoming marriage that forced Duncan to reveal he was her father?
   a. that Beatrice would not be happy with Brian unless her father himself gave her away (Duncan's father, whom Beatrice thought was her own, was dead.)
   b. that Brian would marry an Irish lass (Duncan also revealed that Beatrice's mother was Irish, making Beatrice Irish as well.)

  c. that Beatrice had not told Brian who she really was (which led Brian to believe she was not Duncan's sister but his mistress)

  d. that Beatrice would be joining her mother shortly after she wed (Since Duncan's mother was dead, Beatrice assumed that this meant she would die if she married Brian. Duncan assured her that her biological mother was still alive.)

4. What sort of animal did Duncan keep as a pet at the castle?
  a. tarantula
  b. crocodile (in the moat)
  c. monkey
  d. falcon

5. What curse had been placed on the McKechnie family?
  a. All first-born sons would die as infants.
  b. McKechnie women would go mad after giving birth.
  c. McKechnie women would die giving birth to daughters.
  d. McKechnie fathers would never see their sons become fathers.

6. Why had the curse been placed on the family by Duncan's ancestor Margaret, whose ghost haunted the castle?
  a. Her husband, Angus, had killed her when she gave birth to a girl and not a boy.
  b. Angus had let her die in childbirth, wrongly believing that she was carrying another man's child.
  c. Angus had murdered her to marry his pregnant mistress.
  d. Angus had killed their only son.

7. Which drug lord did the police suspect Duncan of being?
  a. The Spider
  b. Mr. Big
  c. The Piper
  d. The Falcon

8. What had Duncan's first wife, Lilith, done on their wedding night that forced Duncan to have her committed?
   a. She plunged a knife into his back while they were making love.
   b. After sex, she set their bed on fire with Duncan asleep in it.
   c. Rather than go to bed with Duncan, she tried to throw herself out the window.
   d. She drugged Duncan and walled them up in the bedroom together.

9. How did Lilith plan to get away with murdering Shannon?
   a. She planned to frame Duncan for the crime.
   b. She planned to make it look like self-defense.
   c. She planned to make it look like suicide.
   d. She planned to plead insanity.

10. When the plan to kill Shannon fell through, Lilith escaped and bided her time. She waited until Shannon had married Duncan before kidnapping her and dragging her off to Africa. Although Shannon turned up alive years later, Duncan believed that she had been killed by Lilith. What gruesome evidence did Lilith present to Duncan as "proof" of Shannon's death?
    a. the cannibalized remains of a dark-haired woman
    b. a left hand with Shannon's wedding band and engagement ring still on the ring finger
    c. a shrunken head
    d. a human heart

The Men in Emily's Life

When it comes to men, Emily Stewart has had either incredibly bad taste or incredibly bad luck. Half of the men she's slept with have committed murder: James Stenbeck, Tonio Reyes, Brock Lombard, Royce Keller...even Paul Stenbeck killed his own father. And her latest bed partner, Umberto Malzone, may be responsible for the plane crash that killed Damian Grimaldi. Among the nicer guys (meaning nonmurderers) she's slept with have been Craig Montgomery, Evan Walsh, Holden Snyder, and Jef Hamlin. In the quiz below, see if you can find the right man to fill in each blank. If you can, you'll be a few steps ahead of Emily, who has never quite been able to find the right man.

1. _____ was a virgin when he slept with Emily.

2. _____ suffered from multiple personality disorder and had killed his own sister the same night he proposed to Emily.

3. So far, Emily has only married one man, _____.

4. And she cheated on him with his brother-in-law, _____.

5. Twice Emily got involved with _____, who had once been married to her own sister.

6. Emily was not only a bed-partner but a partner-in-crime with _____, who conspired with her to oust Kirk Anderson from Worldwide.

7. For weeks, Emily refused to let her grandmother Ellen set her up with schoolteacher _____, whom she later met on her own and started dating.

8. Although _____ himself belonged to a crime family in Chicago, it was important to him that Emily came from a respectable family.

9. Spending long and late nights together at work led Emily into a brief fling with _____ while his girlfriend, Courtney Baxter, was out of the country.

10. _____ tried to strangle Emily to death.

Celebrity Fans Among Us

In her recent autobiography, *As My World Still Turns*, Eileen Fulton describes meeting opera legend **Renata Tebaldi** backstage at the Metropolitan Opera: "Before Van [pianist and fan **Van Cliburn**] had a chance to introduce me, Renata extended her arms in my direction, crying 'Lisa, Lisa' You bad, bad girl.' I nearly fainted from delight. One of my idols, whom I had loved all my life…was a fan of mine!"

Tebaldi is but one of the many celebrity fans who have tuned into *As the World Turns* over the years. Also included on that list are the late pop artist **Andy Warhol**; horror novelist **Stephen King**; country singer **George Jones**; hockey star **Ron Greschner**; Civil War historian **Shelby Foote**; pianist **Bobby Short**; comedienne **Imogene Coca**, who once did a cameo on the show during the Mr. Big story line, dancer **Fred Astaire**; Queen of the Cowgirls **Dale Evans**, and the Queen of Soul, **Aretha Franklin**. Actress **Catherine O'Hara**, who played Macaulay Culkin's mother in the *Home Alone* movies, started watching the show with her own mother, and basketball player **Cherokee Parks** of the Dallas Mavericks picked up the habit from his wife.

As the World Turns has also been a favorite soap in the White House, watched by First Ladies **Mamie Eisenhower, Betty Ford,** and **Barbara Bush** as well as Jimmy Carter's mother, **Miss Lillian**.

The late **Bette Davis** never expected to get hooked on a soap opera. "I thought anyone who would put on a soap opera at a certain time every day was just wasting his gray matter," she told *Soap Opera Digest*. Once she had the free time, though, she started watching, among other soaps, *As the World Turns* and became a big fan of Kathryn Hays ("very attractive and very talented"), Larry Bryggman ("sensational"), and Eileen Fulton ("I'm mad for Eileen Fulton"). The only part about soaps she didn't care for were the teen story lines. "I don't think they need them. I just say, 'Oh God, get these kids over with and get me back to the people.'"

Also a fan of the show and of Fulton in particular is **Zsa Zsa Gabor**, who started watching the show after she guest-starred on it for a week back in the early eighties. "I played some Italian countess—as usual," she says with a laugh. Of Lisa's many trips down the aisle, Gabor says, "She's almost where I am. I hope she gets there."

See if you can locate all twenty of these celebrity fans in the letter grid below.

```
Y K B P B M F F L Y X B E H S L X P J B
W R G Y A R E T H A F R A N K L I N A E
X R C H E R O K E E P A R K S K Q R F T
D E A A L E J N Z S A Z S A G A B O R T
L N T G M B G V G G I B K S C A K G O Y
R A H V N I T E Y R R B I K R H G L K F
Y T E M A I S D O W E V T A G J R X F O
J A R S T O K S V R A S B D H E A W R R
K T I V C R C N L D G U C R H D R H E D
L E N M A M I E E I S E N H O W E R D A
F B E G O M A T L H L I J P N M M K A L
E A O X C G T N E E P L P O P E M Z S E
Z L H B Z E E L D Q P E I E N P R V T E
J D A E B W B N C Y N H T A A E N Y A V
X I R N D Y C B E H W S U S N R S Y I A
Z F A W F I S F Y C V A N C L I B U R N
R C S O H L Y H Z C O L R W T K S N E S
P Y O F B M C V O G U C W H M O O P J V
X T H O Y R P X Y R M D A A O E U N Q U
E P L E R W F R I Q T X Q F E L E R D L
```

Holden Lily Tight

Of all the couples *As the World Turns* has paired together in the last ten years, none have been more popular than heiress Lily

Walsh and farm boy Holden Snyder. Maybe because no other couples have faced quite the same uphill battle as Holden and Lily. The vast difference in their backgrounds was nothing next to the truth that Holden's sister Iva was Lily's biological mother. And none of Lucinda's many schemes to split the two up worked anywhere near as effectively as the brain surgery that permanently cost Holden his memory and made Lily a stranger to him. Although the fans kept waiting for Holden and Lily to get back together, the writers—prompted by Palo Seganti's growing popularity as Lily's new husband, Damian Grimaldi, and by Jon Hensley's decision to leave the show—did the unthinkable: they split Holden and Lily up for good—at least for the time being.

1. In what capacity was Holden working for Lucinda when he first met Lily?

2. In what subject did Lucinda hire Holden to tutor Lily?

3. Although Holden had stopped pursuing Lily romantically when he discovered the truth about Iva being Lily's mother, what made him change his mind?

4. When Lily took off for Wyoming, Holden took off after her. What had made Lily run away from Oakdale?

5. What medical crisis brought the two of them back to town?

6. What did Lucinda tell Lily that made her break up with Holden?

7. After the breakup, Lily moved in with which of her old boyfriends?

8. Holden in turn jumped into a hasty marriage with Emily Stewart. Why did they get married?

9. After divorcing Emily, Holden attempted a reconciliation with Lily that didn't work out, and he eventually left town and jumped into another rash and ultimately unhappy marriage. Whom did he marry this time?

10. Holden returned to town two years later, and eventually he and Lily got back together. But not before Holden slept with his sister-in-law Julie. Why did Holden sleep with Julie?

11. After Holden married Lily, what tragedy triggered her bout with depression?

12. What secret did Holden discover that sent him racing to New York to confront Julie?

13. What happened to Holden in New York that resulted in his permanent memory loss?

14. After months of trying to make Holden remember their love, Lily finally gave up on him and left town. Prompting that decision was her discovery that both her adoptive mother, Lucinda, and her biological mother, Iva, had kept secrets from her. What secrets had the two women kept?

15. How did Lily attempt to get back at Lucinda for keeping that secret?

16. Holden's memory did not come back, but he did come to realize that he loved Lily. And although she was married to Damian Grimaldi, Lily could not fight her feelings for Holden. Where did they finally make love?

17. How was Lily sidetracked on her way to tell her husband that she was leaving him to go back to Holden?

18. What made Lily change her mind and decide to stay with her husband?

19. Why did Holden leave Oakdale?

20. Holden made a brief return visit and helped Lily deliver her baby. Where did she give birth?

Paging Dr. Dixon: The Malpractice Suit

While under the care of John Dixon, Lisa's seventh husband, Eduardo Grimaldi, was murdered in his hospital bed. Not realizing that Eduardo had been murdered; Lisa blamed John for her husband's death. In her grief, she filed a malpractice suit against John that nearly ripped their families apart.

1. Why had Eduardo been rushed to the emergency room in the first place?

2. Whom did John treat ahead of Eduardo, thus infuriating Lisa?

3. How was Eduardo murdered?

4. Claiming wrongful death, Lisa filed suit against John. How much was she seeking?

5. When Margo advised John to let the insurance company fight Lisa, John revealed that he no longer had malpractice insurance. Why had he let his insurance payments lapse?

6. Whom did John hire to defend him?

7. How did John save the life of Rick Hamlin, the lawyer Lisa hired to handle her case?

8. Lisa agreed to drop the lawsuit under one condition. What was it?

9. After losing the lawsuit, John could not go back to practicing medicine. What job did he take instead?

10. As soon as Lisa learned the truth about what really happened to Eduardo the night he died, she filed a motion to have the judgment against John overturned. How did Lisa discover the truth about what had happened to Eduardo?

Whodunit and Whogotit?

Five of the show's more notorious murder mysteries have been described here with certain details carefully omitted, like the names of the killers and their victims. From the varied clues given in each synopsis, see if you can figure out who the killer turned out to be in each case and who the victim was, *if* there even was a victim.

1. This murder investigation went on for more than a year and led the police through a maze of surrogate pregnancy, organized crime, and corporate takeovers. By the time the killer had finally been identified, it turned out to be the same man who had already been sentenced to prison for the crime.

2. Even though this villain was not really dead, most of Oakdale was suspected of committing his murder—including his ex-wife, who went to prison for the crime. A couple of years later, the woman's son would also go on trial for killing this man. Unlike his mother, who was innocent but went to prison, the son killed his father but got away with it.

3. When this presumed murder victim realized that the wrong person was being tried for his murder, he made a surprise resurrection in the courtroom. It was one of those only-on-daytime murder trials where the defendant walks and the victim gets punished.

4. After this blackmailer's body was found in a block of cement, the police were soon investigating most of Oakdale. The killer, though, was a lot closer to home than the detective leading the investigation cared to discover. He ended up having to arrest his own girlfriend, an ex-porn-actress turned model.

5. The solution to this murder surprised many people—including the killer himself, who had unknowingly killed his own sister. While the killer was on the witness stand, two alternate personalities emerged, one of whom confessed.

Lucinda to the Third Power

Anybody who has been watching *As the World Turns* steadily during the twelve years since Lucinda first arrived in Oakdale should find this puzzle—with no disrespect intended to CBS—as simple as ABC.

1. Lucinda has a total of three daughters, at least one of whom was adopted. Name all three daughters in order of age and note whether each one was adopted or biological.
   a. _____
   b. _____
   c. _____

2. Lucinda has three half siblings, all of whom have gone by different last names. Name all three, first name and last, and indicate which two are twins.
   a. _____
   b. _____
   c. _____

3. Lucinda came to Oakdale with three marriages under her belt. She has only gotten married once on the show, though, to John Dixon. Who (in proper order) were the first three husbands?
   a. _____
   b. _____
   c. _____

4. A woman who knows how to mix business with pleasure, Lucinda has taken three of her executives to bed. Name them.
   a. _____
   b. _____
   c. _____

Broadcast in Stereo

Oakdale may not be a music capital in America, but there are some very strong ties between the show and popular music. In 1995, the Brian McKnight song "Every Beat of My Heart," which was introduced on *As the World Turns*, hit big on *Billboard*'s R&B chart. The show has also given several cast members the chance to show off their musical talents, both as singers and songwriters. A few of them have even managed to parlay their success on daytime into record deals and nightclub performances.

1. Whose theme song was "Every Beat of My Heart"?
   a. Holden and Lily
   b. Damian and Lily
   c. Mike and Rosanna
   d. Kirk and Samantha

2. Which future superstar performed a duet with Jermaine Jackson at the Cinderella Ball in 1984?
   a. his sister, Janet Jackson
   b. Whitney Houston
   c. Mariah Carey
   d. Paula Abdul

3. What song had been used as Hal and Barbara's theme song before Bette Midler recorded her chart-topping version of it?
   a. "The Rose"
   b. "From a Distance"
   c. "Wind Beneath My Wings"
   d. "Do You Wanna Dance?"

4. Which cast member released a self-titled CD in 1995?
   a. Martha Byrne
   b. Scott Holmes
   c. Tamara Tunie
   d. Shawn Christian

5. In 1991, Aretha Franklin sent an invitation to the *As the World Turns* cast to appear in the video for her song "Everyday People." Who was the only cast member to take Franklin up on her offer?
   a. Scott DeFreitas
   b. Eileen Fulton
   c. Anthony Herrera
   d. Lisa Brown

6. Who wrote the song "Penny" that Rosemary Prinz included on her 1966 album *TV's Penny Sings* and released as a single?
   a. Mark Rydell, who played Penny's husband Jeff Baker
   b. Don Hastings, who played Penny's brother Bob
   c. Rosemary Prinz herself
   d. Paul Anka

7. With what song did Rex Smith (who played Darryl Crawford) hit *Billboard*'s Top Ten back in the 1970s?
   a. "You Make Me Feel Like Dancing"
   b. "Seasons in the Sun"
   c. "You Take My Breath Away"
   d. "Sometimes When We Touch"

8. Which actor wrote the song "Warm by Your Side," which was then used as one of the love themes for him and his leading lady?
   a. Jon Hensley for Holden and Lily
   b. Scott Bryce for Craig and Sierra
   c. Scott Holmes for Tom and Margo
   d. Frank Runyeon for Steve and Betsy

9. Which of the following performed a duet with Patti Austin on the show?
   a. James Ingram
   b. Luther Vandross
   c. Johnny Mathis
   d. Bill Medley of the Righteous Brothers

10. As nurse/chanteuse Lyla Montgomery, Anne Sward often performed the song that became recognized as Lyla and Casey's theme song. What was the title of it?
    a. "Till I Found You"
    b. "From Now on"
    c. "You Are My Dream"
    d. "I've Stopped Running"

11. In 1994, Martha Byrne, Scott Holmes, and Tamara Tunie sang on a CD with actors from different soaps recording what kind of music?
    a. love ballads
    b. show tunes
    c. children's songs
    d. Christmas carols

12. On what CD will you find the song "Papa Come Quick (Jody and Chico)" that includes the lyrics "Mama's been cryin' in the kitchen since mornin' / She cried right through *As the World Turns*"?
    a. Bruce Springsteen's *The River*
    b. Reba McEntire's *Read My Mind*
    c. John Cougar Mellencamp's *American Fool*
    d. Bonnie Raitt's *Luck of the Draw*

Simply Barbara

After James Stenbeck's presumed death in the early eighties, Barbara Ryan's character did a complete turnaround from victim to vixen. Once the cheated-upon wife, she proceeded to make herself the other woman in a number of Oakdale's more troubled marriages. While Barbara has toned down her act in recent years, she still has a mental block against honesty, a fault that keeps coming between her and Hal Munson.

1. How did Barbara add to Tom and Margo's marital problems back in the mid 1980s?

2. Why did Lucinda offer to back Barbara's fashion line only if she broke off her affair with Tonio Reyes?

3. Why did Barbara bring Duncan McKechnie to town?

4. When Bob and Kim discovered that their daughter Sabrina had not died at birth but was actually alive, why did Barbara have a hard time accepting her into the family?

5. What secret did Barbara keep from Hal while they were first married?

6. What revelation ended Hal and Barbara's first marriage?

7. After Hal left her, Barbara took up with a James Stenbeck–like suitor named Gavin Kruger, a shady businessman with serious connections to the mob. For what crime was Gavin Kruger convicted?

8. Why did Barbara blame her sister Frannie for Hal's presumed death?

9. After Hal and Barbara remarried, why did she pretend that she was being stalked?

10. What caused Hal and Barbara's latest reconciliation attempt to fail?

11. To how many of her three children's fathers was Barbara married at the time of their conception?

12. What two fashion lines carry Barbara's name?

The World of Eileen Fulton

In 1995, commemorating the thirty-fifth anniversary of her joining the cast of *As the World Turns*, Eileen Fulton published her second autobiography, *As My World Still Turns: The Uncensored Memoirs of America's Soap Opera Queen*. Although she has spent more than half her life taking Lisa through multiple marriages, affairs, murder attempts, and courtroom trials, Fulton has managed to lead a fairly interesting life outside the CBS studios.

1. While Fulton had originally considered calling herself Amanda Ashton, she finally settled on the professional name Eileen Fulton. "Fulton" she had taken from her family history. "Eileen" came from a suggestion made by her first husband. Her husband had not actually suggested the name Eileen itself, but Fulton could not hear him correctly over the telephone. What name had he actually suggested she use for her career?
   a. Aileen
   b. Ellen
   c. Irene
   d. Arlene

2. What does the title *Girl of the Night* refer to?
   a. the first play she did on Broadway
   b. the movie she made her film debut in
   c. the first prime-time TV series she starred in
   d. the first soap opera she ever landed a role on

3. What was the title of the first autobiography Eileen Fulton published, in 1970?
   a. *My World and Welcome to It*
   b. *Queen of the World*
   c. *The Confessions of Lisa Miller Hughes*
   d. *How My World Turns*

4. Fulton has also written a number of novels in what genre?
   a. contemporary romance
   b. historical romance
   c. murder mystery
   d. young adult

5. For what magazine did Fulton once write a five-hundred-word comic essay titled "Nipples," describing her body's response to the low temperature in the CBS studios?
   a. *Playboy*
   b. *TV Guide*
   c. *Cosmopolitan*
   d. *The National Lampoon*

6. What magazine did Fulton sue for running a photo of a naked look-alike with the caption "Can this be *our* Eileen Fulton"?
   a. *The National Enquirer*
   b. *Penthouse*
   c. *Celebrity Sleuth*
   d. *Spy*

7. On what talk show did Fulton nearly come to blows with another guest, who accused her of sleeping her way to success?
   a. *Geraldo*
   b. *Donahue*
   c. *The Oprah Winfrey Show*
   d. *Live with Regis and Kathie Lee*

8. How many times has Fulton been married in real life?
   a. two
   b. three
   c. never
   d. seven, the same as Lisa

9. What was the name of Fulton's first album, released in 1969?
   a. *Eileen Fulton's World of Music*
   b. *Same Old World*
   c. *Siren's Song*
   d. *World on a String*

10. Which of all Lisa's story lines has Fulton hated playing the most?

    a. Lisa's infidelity while married to Bob Hughes

    b. Lisa's opposition to an interracial marriage

    c. Lisa's menopause story line

    d. Lisa's hysterical pregnancy

Rosanna, Rosanna

In 1992, the writers tried to re-create the Holden and Lily story, by pairing farmhand Hutch Hutchison up with a reluctant heiress named Rosanna Cabot. Although the Hutch-Rosanna romance never took off the way Holden and Lily's story did, Rosanna did emerge as one of the most popular young characters on the show.

  1. Corporate climber Evan Walsh set his sights on Rosanna when he realized that she was millionaire Alexander Cabot's missing daughter. How did Evan discover Rosanna's identity?

  2. What kind of business did Rosanna's father run?

  3. What did Evan's mother, Edwina, tell him that made him cool his relationship with Rosanna?

  4. The first time Rosanna met Mike Kasnoff, the two of them got into a fight. What was the argument about?

  5. What family secret did Rosanna learn when she went to her mother's hometown of Musselshell, Montana?

  6. Why did Rosanna blame Mike for her father's death?

  7. How did Scott Eldridge help bilk Rosanna out of $100,000?

  8. When Mike proposed to Rosanna in Florida, where did he hide the engagement ring?

  9. What information did Rosanna learn on the day of her wedding to Mike that made her call off the wedding?

10. What did Rosanna become addicted to after breaking up with Mike?

Social Issues of the Day

After Anne Sward (who played Lyla Peretti) got involved with the rights of Native Americans, she approached head writer Doug Marland about incorporating the plight of the Native American into her plotline. Lyla soon found herself taking in a Native American boarder and fighting with her millionaire fiancé, Cal Stricklyn, about his plans to drill for oil on sacred ground. It was but one of many social issues *As the World Turns* has tackled in recent memory. Among the others have been bulimia, teen alcoholism, AIDS, Alzheimer's disease and, interracial marriage.

1. Which of the following characters has never suffered from bulimia?
   a. Frannie Hughes
   b. Meg Snyder
   c. Connor Walsh
   d. Courtney Baxter

2. To whom in Oakdale did Hank Eliot first admit that he was gay?
   a. Iva Snyder
   b. Barbara Ryan
   c. Emily Stewart
   d. Lily Walsh

3. When Casey Peretti was dying from encephalitis, he refused to allow himself to be kept alive by machines. Whom did he ask to disconnect his life support system?
   a. his wife, Lyla
   b. his stepdaughter Margo
   c. Bob Hughes
   d. John Dixon

4. Which character donated an egg so that her mother, who could no longer conceive, could give her husband a baby?
   a. Margo Hughes
   b. Marcy Thompson
   c. Emily Stewart
   d. Ellie Snyder

5. After Henry Lange committed suicide, Caleb Snyder was arrested for his murder. During the trial, Lange's daughter Angel testified that her father had sexually abused her for many years. What other revelation came out during her testimony?
   a. Her father had once impregnated her.
   b. Her father had paid a doctor to sterilize her.
   c. Her father had once given her a venereal disease.
   d. Her father had also sexually abused her brothers.

6. Which character developed a drinking problem while still a teenager?
   a. Andy Dixon
   b. Emily Stewart
   c. Duke Kramer
   d. Lien Hughes

7. Kim's first guest when her talk show *Patterns* debuted was psychiatrist Lynn Michaels. What topic did they discuss that led one of the show's teen characters to seek help?
   a. eating disorders
   b. teen suicide
   c. rising teen pregnancy rates
   d. steroid use among athletes

8. Which of their friends initially had trouble accepting the interracial relationship between Scotsman Duncan McKechnie and Jessica Griffin, an African-American lawyer?
   a. Tom Hughes
   b. Kirk Anderson

   c. Lisa Mitchell
   d. Lucinda Walsh

9. Margo Hughes's horror over being raped was compounded
   when she learned that her rapist was HIV-positive. What was
   the name of the ex-convict who raped Margo?
   a. Gil Stallings
   b. Bernard Grayson
   c. Doug Cummings
   d. Elroy Nevins

10. Which recently deceased character battled Alzheimer's
    disease?
    a. Dave Stewart
    b. Eduardo Grimaldi
    c. Dan McCloskey
    d. Alexander Cabot

A Family Tree Grows in Oakdale

When *As the World Turns* debuted in 1956, at the heart of the
show was the Hughes family. From Edith's affair with Jim Lowell
to Penny's romance with Jeff Baker to Bob Hughes's impetuous
and unhappy marriage to Lisa Miller, the Hugheses dominated
the show through the fifties and better part of the sixties. In the
seventies, the Stewarts emerged as the show's focus family, and
in the eighties, that focus shifted to the Snyders. One by one,
though, the Snyders have all but vanished from Oakdale, and only
a few scattered Stewarts are still living in town. But the Hughes
family survives. Forty years and two generations after the show's
first episode aired, the Hughes family remains at the core of life
in Oakdale.

1. Who is the oldest of Bob Hughes's biological grandchildren?
   a. Adam Hughes
   b. Casey Hughes

    c. Lien Hughes
    d. Paul Ryan

2. Which of his daughter's fiancés shot Bob Hughes and later held him and Susan Stewart hostage?
    a. Tonio Reyes
    b. Seth Snyder
    c. Doug Cummings
    d. Darryl Crawford

3. Which of Andy's girlfriends poisoned Kim's tea so that she could take over Kim's talk show?
    a. Julie Wendall
    b. Courtney Baxter
    c. Meg Snyder
    d. Janice Maxwell

4. From what Ivy League college did Frannie Hughes flunk out?
    a. Harvard
    b. Yale
    c. Princeton
    d. Columbia

5. In what European city did Frannie first spot her look-alike half-sister/cousin Sabrina?
    a. Venice
    b. Berlin
    c. Monte Carlo
    d. London

6. Bob's father, Chris, died shortly after celebrating what event in his life?
    a. his seventy-fifth birthday
    b. his fiftieth wedding anniversary to Nancy
    c. the birth of his first great-grandchild
    d. his retirement from practicing law

7. How many years passed between Chris's death and Nancy's marriage to police lieutenant Dan McCloskey?
   a. half a year
   b. a year
   c. two years
   d. three years

8. Tom Hughes is Andy Dixon's brother-in-law through his marriage to Andy's half sister Margo. How else are the two related?
   a. They are stepbrothers.
   b. Tom is Andy's half brother on the other side.
   c. They are cousins.
   d. Tom is Andy's uncle.

9. Who delivered Christopher Hughes?
   a. John Dixon
   b. Margo Hughes
   c. Casey Peretti
   d. his father, Bob

10. In what Asian country was Lien Hughes born?
    a. China
    b. Japan
    c. Vietnam
    d. Korea

Current Events

When *As the World Turns* debuted in 1956, there were approximately a dozen cast members and only one main plot, Edith Hughes's affair with Jim Lowell. By 1996, the cast has almost tripled in size with close to a dozen plotlines going on at any one time. The following ten questions come from events that have happened in Oakdale during the first half of 1996.

1. How did John Dixon get even with Lisa Grimaldi for the malpractice suit she brought against him?

2. How did Damian Grimaldi die?

3. How was Samantha Anderson blinded?

4. Where did Lisa meet Martin Chedwin?

5. Where did Connor and Mark make love?

6. How was Connor's husband Cal paralyzed?

7. Who was nearly killed by a bomb planted in Tom Hughes's car?

8. How did Mac McCloskey die?

9. Why did Jessica Griffin represent a gun runner for a white supremacist organization?

10. How did Carly Tenney lose her baby?

World History Final Exam

The following twenty-five questions cover *As the World Turns*'s history onscreen and off from 1956 all the way through to the present day. Fifteen or more correct answers are needed for a passing grade. Anyone scoring lower than that should be spending a little less time at the library and a little more time in front of the TV.

1. Which of the following was *As the World Turns* the first daytime soap opera to feature?
   a. an interracial marriage
   b. a teenage alcoholic
   c. a legal abortion
   d. a gay leading man

2. Which actor/actress received so much hate mail, including death threats, back in the 1960s that a bodyguard was hired to protect him/her?
   a. Anthony Herrera (James Stenbeck)
   b. Larry Bryggman (John Dixon)
   c. Eileen Fulton (Lisa Miller)
   d. Barbara Rodell (Joyce Colman)

3. How many years did it take *As the World Turns* to become the number one ranked soap opera?
   a. one
   b. two
   c. five
   d. ten

4. How many years did it then stay at the top of the ratings?
   a. two
   b. five
   c. ten
   d. twenty

5. In 1962, Millette Alexander created the role of Sylvia Hill, a nurse dying of lupus. Why did the writers change their plans to have Sylvia die of lupus?
   a. She became too popular with the audience to let her go.
   b. Millette Alexander got engaged to the producer's son.
   c. Lupus patients started calling the show, afraid they were going to die as well.
   d. For plot reasons, they needed to kill her off more quickly.

6. Whose 1962 death did *TV Guide* describe as "the car accident that shook the nation"?
   a. Jim Lowell's
   b. Edith Hughes's
   c. Jeff Baker's
   d. Betty Stewart's

7. Geoffrey Lumb played the same character, a lawyer, not only on *As the World Turns* but on *The Brighter Day* and *Another World* as well, both of them also created by Irna Phillips. What was the name of the character Lumb played?
   a. Kirk Anderson
   b. Jeff Baker
   c. Tim Cole
   d. Mitchell Dru

8. What unique clause did Fulton have written into her contract back in the 1970s?
   a. "The Widow Clause" ensuring that Lisa would never be widowed again.
   b. "The Grandmother Clause" preventing the writers from making Lisa a grandmother.
   c. "The Underwear Clause" stipulating that Fulton never had to appear onscreen in anything less than a nightgown.
   d. "The August Clause" allowing Fulton to take off the full month of August every year.

9. The freak accident that claimed Liz Talbot Stewart's life has long been cited as one of the oddest on daytime. What happened to her?
   a. A potted plant fell from a balcony and hit her on the head.
   b. Her scarf got caught in an electric fan and strangled her to death.
   c. She fell *up* (not down) a flight of stairs and ruptured her liver when she landed.
   d. She got locked in a bank vault and suffocated.

10. In December of 1975, *As the World Turns* expanded to an hour. What other major change happened that same year?
   a. The show stopped airing live.
   b. The show began airing in color.

c. The show moved from the afternoon to the late morning.

d. For six months, the show experimented with filming rather than taping each episode.

11. While Eileen Fulton is the definitive Lisa, she is not the only actress to have played the role. Which of the following actresses has never played Lisa?
    a. Jane Powell
    b. Betsy von Furstenberg
    c. Robin Strasser
    d. Pamela King

12. Which current cast member has written dialogue for the show under the pseudonym J. J. Matthew?
    a. Don Hastings
    b. Kathryn Hays
    c. Larry Bryggman
    d. Tom Wiggin

13. Which of the show's future headwriters played Lisa's obstetrician during the Phantom Fetus story line, in which Lisa experienced a hysterical pregnancy?
    a. Irna Phillips
    b. Doug Marland
    c. Agnes Nixon
    d. Bill Bell

14. In 1985, what event brought original cast member Rosemary Prinz back to the show after a seventeen-year absence?
    a. A Hughes family reunion
    b. Bob and Kim's wedding
    c. Nancy Hughes's open heart surgery
    d. Chris Hughes's funeral

15. Why did head writer Doug Marland change his plans for Hank Eliot, a gay character, to die of AIDS?
    a. The character had grown too popular.
    b. Viewer reaction to him was so negative that Marland

had to write him off more quickly than an AIDS story necessitated.

c. Marland worried that the story line might send out the message that all gay men get AIDS.

d. Two other shows introduced AIDS story lines at the same time.

16. The adventure story line in which Tom Hughes and Margo Montgomery were imprisoned by drug dealer Mr. Big featured one of the most unusual and elaborate sets ever built for daytime: Mr. Big's "house of horrors," which was filled with booby-trapped scenes from what popular children's story?

a. *Alice in Wonderland*
b. *Peter Pan*
c. *Cinderella*
d. *The Wizard of Oz*

17. What 1992 story line reintroduced characters from the *As the World Turns* spin-off, *Our Private World?*

a. The discovery that Sabrina Hughes had not died in childbirth.

b. The revelation that Lisa had given birth to another son, Scott Eldridge.

c. The introduction of Eduardo Grimaldi as John Eldridge's long-lost twin.

d. Lisa's arrest for the murder of her ex-husband John Eldridge.

18. What current soap opera was initially conceived of as a spin-off from *As the World Turns?*

a. *Another World*
b. *All My Children*
c. *The Young and the Restless*
d. *Days of Our Lives*

19. How many major Emmy awards (meaning those awarded for acting, writing, directing, and best show) has *As the World Turns* won?

   a. eight
   b. twelve
   c. seventeen
   d. twenty-one

20. Which of the following scenes prompted the show to open that day's episode with a warning that the shows contents would be graphic in detail?

   a. Angel Lange's testimony of being sexually abused by her father.
   b. Hans's kidnapping of Lily.
   c. The murder of Eduardo Grimaldi.
   d. Margo's rape.

21. On February 1, 1994, a news report on ice skater Tonya Harding interrupted the East Coast airing of *As the World Turns*, causing the switchboards at CBS to light up with complaints. The very next day, for the first time in the show's history, the episode was rerun in its entirety. What had happened that day that the producers considered so important for fans to see?

   a. Lisa married Eduardo Grimaldi.
   b. Margo received the results of her HIV test.
   c. Lily told Holden that she was ending her marriage to Damian to be with him.
   d. Carolyn Crawford's killer was revealed.

22. What was so odd about Mary Ellen Stuart being cast as Frannie Hughes and Claire Beckman later being cast as her cousin/half-sister Sabrina?

   a. Stuart and Beckman are cousins in real life.
   b. Beckman had originally auditioned to play Frannie, and Stuart to play Sabrina.

    c. The two had previously played half sisters Emily and Betsy Stewart.

    d. Both Frannie and Sabrina had originally been played as a dual role by one actress.

23. Which of the following props was donated to the Smithsonian Institute?

    a. Judge Lowell's gavel

    b. Nancy Hughes's coffeepot

    c. Penny's bouquet from her second marriage to Jeff Baker

    d. Lisa's first wedding dress

24. *As the World Turns* marked its anniversary in 1986 with what onscreen celebration?

    a. A surprise party for Bob Hughes's fiftieth birthday

    b. the Cinderella Ball

    c. Chris and Nancy Hughes's fiftieth wedding anniversary

    d. Oakdale's tricentennial

25. Approximately how many episodes of the show have aired?

    a. 5,000

    b. 10,000

    c. 20,000

    d. 25,000

Bonus. Although Carol Burnett was an *All My Children* fan, her variety show featured a recurring *As the World Turns* spoof. What was the sketch titled?

    a. *As the Worm Turns*

    b. *As the World Burns*

    c. *As the Stomach Turns*

    d. *As the Butter Churns*

Photo Quiz

1. On April 12, 1985, Bob Hughes and Kim Reynolds (Don Hastings and Kathryn Hays, pictured above) finally tied the knot. Although they had fallen in love when Kim was first introduced on the show in 1972, the two of them had spent more than a decade not only apart but in marriages to other people. Exactly how many times had they each been married to other people?

2. Next to Meg Ryan, Marisa Tomei (pictured here with fashion designer Albert Capraro), is arguably the most successful actress to have started out on *As the World Turns*. Having played Marcy Thompson on the show from 1983-85, Tomei is one the few former soap actors to ever win an Academy Award. For what movie did she win the Oscar as Best Supporting Actress?

3. One of the show's most popular triangles of all time has been that of Steve Andropolous, Betsy Stewart, and Craig Montgomery (Frank Runyeon, Meg Ryan, and Scott Bryce, pictured above). How did Diana McColl (Kim Ulrich, pictured in insert) figure into the storyline?

4. In 1982, while other soap operas were delving into science fiction and tales of espionage, *As the World Turns* itself decided to try something different. Barbara Ryan began having visions of herself and husband James Stenbeck (Anthony Herrera, pictured above with Jacqueline Schultz) as 18th Century characters whose lives paralleled their own. What Oakdale heroine also figured into Barbara's visions as Deidre, the servant girl?

5. What was the name of Barbara's (Colleen Zenk Pinter, pictured here) 18th Century counterpart?

6. It was in these visions that Barbara first "saw" Gunnar St. Clair (Hugo Napier, pictured here), who was later introduced into the present day storyline as James's orphaned cousin. What was the secret connection between James and Gunnar that James would have killed to keep people from discovering?

7. In the mid-1980s, stunt casting had become a trend on the
soaps. Among the many primetime stars who showed up on
daytime was Abe Vigoda (pictured here with Don Hastings,
Kathryn Hays, and fellow guest star Lilia Skala). On what
1970s sitcom had Vigoda made a name for himself?

8. Although Hutch Hutchison and Rosanna Cabot (Judson Mills and Yvonne Perry, pictured here) never really took off as a couple, Perry herself emerged as one of the hottest stars on daytime. In 1993, she won the first *Soap Opera Digest* Award ever given to *As the World Turns* in what category?

9. Since 1960, when Eileen Fulton (pictured here) joined the show, troublemaker Lisa Miller has dominated much of the action. She was back on top in 1995 with the show's best storyline of the year: Lisa's malpractice suit against John Dixon. As hard as it is to imagine Oakdale without Lisa, Fulton has not only considered leaving in the past, she's gone and done it. How many times has she quit the show "forever"?

Answers

The Beginning of the World
1. d   2. d   3. b   4. a   5. c   6. c   7. a   8. b   9. d   10. a   11. c   12. c   13. d   14. a   15. d

As TV Guide *Summed It Up...*
"Ruth Warrick stars in a new daily half-hour dramatic series dealing with the problems and accomplishments of a family. Don MacLaughlin [also stars]."

Lisa Miller Hughes, et cetera: The Early Years
1. d   2. a   3. a   4. c   5. d   6. c   7. b   8. a   9. c   10. b

In Another Life
1. h   2. e   3. f   4. i   5. j   6. c   7. d   8. a   9. b   10. g

Ellen's Sordid Past
1. c   2. b   3. c   4. a   5. a   6. d   7. a   8. a   9. b   10. a

Love That Bob
1. c   2. c   3. b   4. a   5. c   6. a   7. d   8. c   9. c   10. d

A Penny for Your Thoughts
1. c   2. b   3. b   4. c   5. a   6. c   7. d   8. b   9. d   10. b

Lisa's Husband Search
In alphabetical order, Lisa's husbands have been: Grant Colman, Bob Hughes, John Eldridge, Eduardo Grimaldi, Whit McColl, Earl Mitchell, and Michael Shea.

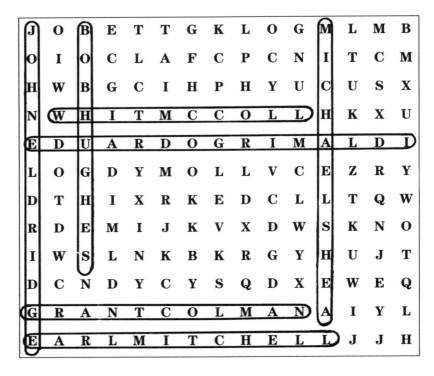

J	O	B	E	T	T	G	K	L	O	G	M	L	M	B
O	I	O	C	L	A	F	C	P	C	N	I	T	C	M
H	W	B	G	C	I	H	P	H	Y	U	C	U	S	X
N	W	H	I	T	M	C	C	O	L	L	H	K	X	U
E	D	U	A	R	D	O	G	R	I	M	A	L	D	D
L	O	G	D	Y	M	O	L	L	V	C	E	Z	R	Y
D	T	H	I	X	R	K	E	D	C	L	L	T	Q	W
R	D	E	M	I	J	K	V	X	D	W	S	K	N	O
I	W	S	L	N	K	B	K	R	G	Y	H	U	J	T
D	C	N	D	Y	C	Y	S	Q	D	X	E	W	E	Q
G	R	A	N	T	C	O	L	M	A	N	A	I	Y	L
E	A	R	L	M	I	T	C	H	E	L	L	J	J	H

The First Lady of Daytime
1. a   2. c   3. c   4. b   5. c   6. b   7. d   8. b   9. b   10. a

The Prime-Time Spin-Off
1. c   2. b   3. d   4. c   5. b

The Marriage Route
Jim Lowell was married to **Claire Lowell**, who, after Jim's death, married and divorced **Michael Shea**, who later married **Lisa Hughes**, who had previously been married to **Bob Hughes**, who is currently married to **Kim Hughes**, who was widowed by **Dan Stewart**, who had also once been married to **Susan Stewart**, who later married and recently separated from Larry McDermott.

Lisa Miller Hughes, et cetera: Shea's Rebellion
1. d   2. c   3. a   4. c   5. d   6. a   7. d   8. a   9. d   10. a

Bob and Kim
1. Florida.   2. Bob had already gone back to her sister Jennifer, who was also pregnant with his child.   3. The baby, a girl, was switched with a baby who had died at birth, and grew up in England. Bob and Kim were reunited with their daughter Sabrina many years later.   4. He was in a car accident.   5. When Kim's then suitor, a government agent named Raymond Speer, took her to Amsterdam with him on a mission, Bob feared for her safety and went jetting after her. Bob realized that his concern for Kim went deeper than simple friendship.   6. At the Stewart cabin during a snowstorm.   7. Still unaware that their first child had not died at birth, Kim was afraid that she was not going to be able to carry the baby to term and didn't want to get Bob's hopes up.   8. Bob "rescued" Laura in the park from what he thought was a mugger. After that, Laura became fixated on building a life with Bob.   9. Laura took a job as the babysitter for Bob and Kim's new son, Christopher.   10. Susan Stewart.

As Irna Phillips Put It...
"As the world turns, we know the bleakness of winter, the promise of spring, the fullness of summer, and the harvest of autumn....The cycle of life is complete....What is true of the world, nature, is also true of man. He too has his cycle."

The Reign of the Stewarts
1. a   2. c   3. c   4. b   5. a   6. a   7. b   8. d   9. b   10. c   11. a   12. c   13. b   14. d   15. c   16. c   17. a   18. d   19. c   20. a

Paging Dr. Dixon: Marriage to Kim
1. b   2. a   3. a   4. c   5. a   6. c   7. d   8. b   9. b   10. c

How Original
1. Helen Wagner: Original.   2. Patricia Bruder took over the role of Ellen Lowell Stewart from Wendy Drew, who had played her from 1956 to 1960; Bruder has played her ever since.   3. Don

Hastings was actually the third actor to play Bob Hughes.
4. Eileen Fulton: Original, but other actresses have played the
role during her varied absences. 5. Kathryn Hays: Original, but
Patty McCormack also played it from 1975 to 1976. 6. Larry
Bryggman: Original. 7. Marie Masters was the fifth actress to
play Susan Stewart. 8. Tom Wiggin: Original. 9. Martha Byrne
almost landed the role of Lily when it was first created, but Lucy
Deakins got it instead; when *As the World Turns* replaced Lucy,
Martha was the obvious choice. 10. Colleen Zenk Pinter joined
As the World Turns as a grown-up Barbara in 1978; as a child,
Barbara had been played previously by three actresses.

Something Wicked This Way Comes
1. b   2. a   3. b   4. a   5. d   6. d   7. b   8. d   9. c   10. c

The Widow Kim
1. a   2. b   3. d   4. b   5. a   6. c   7. b   8. c   9. a   10. c

Oakdale and Points Beyond
1. f   2. g   3. l   4. a   5. j   6. k   7. d   8. e   9. b   10. i   11. h   12. c

Father's Day

Bob Hughes

Child: *Tom Hughes*
Mother: *Lisa Miller Hughes*
Married? *yes*

Child: *Sabrina Fullerton*
Mother: *Kim Reynolds*
Married? *no*

Child: *Frannie Hughes*
Mother: *Jennifer Ryan
Hughes*
Married? *yes*

John Dixon

Child: *Margo Montgomery
Hughes*
Mother: *Lyla Montgomery*
Married? *no*

Child: *Andy Dixon*
Mother: *Kim Reynolds
Dixon*
Married? *yes*

Child: *Ian ("Duke") Kramer*
Mother: *Rosemary Kramer*
Married? *no*

Child: *Christopher Hughes*
Mother: *Kim Reynolds*
Hughes
Married? *yes*

Martin John ("M.J.") Snyder
Mother: *Iva Snyder*
Married? *no*

Satan's Younger Brother
1. c 2. b 3. c 4. a 5. c 6. d 7. b 8. d 9. c 10. a

Separating the Actor From the Role
1. Actor's name: ELIZABETH HUBBARD/ Character's name: LUCINDA WALSH
2. Actor's name: DON HASTINGS/ Character's name: BOB HUGHES
3. Actor's name: MAURA WEST/ Character's name: CARLY TENNEY
4. Actor's name: SCOTT HOLMES/ Character's name: TOM HUGHES
5. Actor's name: COLLEEN ZENK PINTER/ Character's name: BARBARA RYAN
6. Actor's name: LARRY BRYGGMAN/ Character's name: JOHN DIXON
7. Actors name: KATHRYN HAYS/ Character's name: KIM HUGHES
8. Actor's name: SHAWN CHRISTIAN/ Character's name: MIKE KASNOFF
9. Actor's name: KELLEY MENIGHAN/ Character's name: EMILY STEWART
10. Actor's name: TOM WIGGIN/ Character's name: KIRK ANDERSON

True Love
1. a 2. b 3. b 4. d 5. d 6. b 7. a 8. c 9. d 10. a

Paging Dr. Dixon: The War With James Stenbeck
1. He tried to run him down in a parking garage. 2. James was afraid that John would tell Barbara about his (James's) affair with Margo. 3. He was temporarily blinded. 4. John taped a

conversation between Ariel Aldrin and James Stenbeck that revealed the truth. 5. Karen Haines. 6. John was married to Ariel Aldrin, who it turned out was James's half sister. 7. Dee Stewart. 8. In the courtroom during the murder trial. 9. John had to work part-time at a prison hospital for two years. 10. James's son Paul, who was best friends with John's son Andy.

The Many Faces of Tom Hughes
1. a   2. c   3. b   4. b   5. d

Many a Margo
1. HBS.   2. HBS.   3. MC.   4. HBS.   5. ED.   6. ED.   7. GO'C.
8. MC.   9. MC.   10. ED.

To Hollywood and Back
1. c   2. b   3. b   4. c   5. d   6. c   7. d   8. d   9. a   10. c   11. a   12. c
13. a   14. c   15. d

To Hollywood and Back—The Sequel, Starring Meg Ryan
1. b   2. a   3. c   4. d   5. d

Paging Dr. Dixon: The Rape Trial
1. Ian McFarland had died of a heart attack while making love to Dee. 2. John, who was Ian's doctor, learned the circumstances of his death and agreed to keep them secret. 3. Brad Hollister. 4. Brad married her sister Annie. 5. His jealous rages over her feelings for Brad. 6. Tom Hughes. 7. Maggie Crawford. 8. That John was Margo's father. 9. That she had consented to the sex with John—but only because in the darkness she thought he was Brad. 10. *The Outsider.*

Oakdale's Answer to Luke and Laura
1. c   2. a   3. c   4. b   5. d   6. c   7. b   8. b   9. a   10. d

Kim's Secret Admirer
1. c   2. c   3. b   4. a   5. d   6. d   7. c   8. a   9. b   10. b

Hand-Me-Down Lovers
1. Scott Eldridge. 2. Duke Kramer and Andy Dixon; and Caleb and Holden Snyder. 3. Liz Talbot. 4. John Eldridge. 5. Don Hughes. 6. Craig Montgomery. 7. Craig Montgomery and John Dixon. 8. Emily Stewart. 9. Annie and Dee Stewart. 10. Bob Hughes.

Square Dancing by the Snyder Pond
1. John Dixon. 2. Craig Montgomery and Kirk Anderson. 3. Lily Walsh, Julie Wendall, and Angel Lange. 4. Angel Lange. 5. Seth.

James Stenbeck, Back From Hell
1. b   2. c   3. a   4. b   5. a   6. b   7. d   8. c   9. b   10. a

The Prime-Time Exchange Program
1. a   2. d   3. c   4. a   5. d   6. c   7. b   8. c   9. b   10. a

Lisa Miller Hughes, et cetera: A Woman of Mystery
1. c   2. c   3. b   4. b   5. d   6. c   7. d.   8. a   9. d   10. a

No Family Resemblance Whatsoever
1. John Eldridge (Husband Number 2), which Coster played on *As the World Turns* and *Our Private World*, and Eduardo Grimaldi (Husband Number 7). 2. Melinda Gray. 3. Mark Galloway. 4. Glynnis O'Connor. 5. Carolyn Crawford.

A.K.A.
1. Mary Ellen Walters. 2. Mr. Big. 3. James Stenbeck. 4. Rod Landry. 5. David Stewart. 6. Right before losing his memory, Holden had learned that his sister Iva's adopted son Aaron was in fact his own biological son. 7. Jeff Baker. 8. She had flown Air Shannon and landed at O'Hare International Airport in Chicago. 9. Amber D'amour. 10. Diego Santana.

Name Droppers
1. d   2. c   3. b   4. b (Helen Hayes's and Isaac Hayes's names were misspelled on purpose to throw you off.)   5. Marie Masters.

John and Lucinda's Love/Hate/Love Affair
1. a   2. d   3. c   4. a   5. b   6. c   7. c   8. d   9. c   10. b

An Honor Just to Be Nominated

1. Twice (1987 and 1991). 2. Outstanding Juvenile/Young Man in a Daytime Drama Series. (The award has since been renamed Outstanding Younger Leading Actor.) 3. Scott Bryce, who played Craig Montgomery. 4. Two (1984 and 1987). 5. Julianne Moore was named outstanding Ingenue in 1988 for her portrayal of look-alike half-sisters/first-cousins Frannie Hughes and Sabrina Fullerton. 6. In 1977, Spencer was nomimated for the Outstanding Writing for a Daytime Drama Emmy as part of the show's writing team. 7. John Wesley Shipp, who played Doug Cummings. 8. Tom Hughes. (Justin Deas won the Outstanding Supporting Actor Emmy in 1984; Gregg Marx won the same award for playing Tom in 1987.) 9. Martha Byrne, who won the Emmy as Outstanding Ingenue in 1987. (While Elizabeth Hubbard has won two daytime Emmys, neither of them was awarded for her work on *As the World Turns*.) 10. Agnes Nixon in 1981, Bill Bell in 1992, and Doug Marland posthumously in 1993. (*As the World Turns*'s first director, the late Ted Corday, and his wife, Betty, were given the Trustees Award in 1995, mainly for their work on *Days of Our Lives*.)

Worth Quoting

1. c   2. a   3. b   4. c   5. a   6. d   7. b   8. a   9. d   10. c

From Lucinda's Own Lips

1. Emma Snyder. 2. Emily Stewart had donated one of her eggs so that her mother, Susan, could give her younger husband Larry a child. 3. Hal Munson. 4. Craig Montgomery. 5. Lisa Mitchell.

The Haunting of McKechnie Castle

1. a   2. b   3. b   4. d   5. c   6. b   7. d   8. a   9. a   10. c

The Men in Emily's Life

1. Paul Stenbeck   2. Royce Keller   3. Holden Snyder   4. Tonio Reyes   5. Craig Montgomery   6. Umberto Malzone   7. Jef Hamlin   8. Brock Lombard   9. Evan Walsh   10. James Stenbeck

Celebrity Fans Among Us

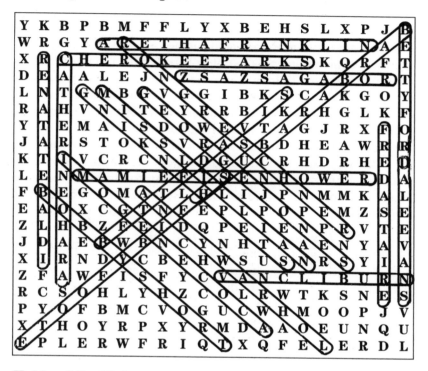

Holden Lily Tight

1. Stablehand. 2. Math. 3. He learned that Iva was adopted, which meant that Lily was not biologically related to him. 4. Lily learned the truth about her parentage: that Iva Snyder was her mother and that Lucinda's new stablehand, Rod Landry, was her father, Josh Snyder. 5. Holden's mother/Lily's grandmother Emma suffered a heart attack. 6. Lucinda told Lily that Holden had known all along about Iva being her mother. 7. Dusty Donovan. 8. Emily wanted a father for the baby she was carrying, which was really James Stenbeck's; Holden wanted Emily's trust fund to start up a business with Tonio Reyes. 9. Angel Lange. 10. In a drunken stupor, Holden imagined that Julie was Lily. 11. She suffered a miscarriage. 12. Holden over-

heard Iva discussing the fact that her adopted son Aaron was really Holden's son from his drunken night with Julie. 13. He was mugged and then run down by his attackers. The subsequent brain surgery caused permanent memory loss. 14. Lily learned that Iva's adopted son was really Holden's child and that Lucinda had known where Holden was for weeks while he was missing after the accident. 15. She filed papers to legally "annul" Lucinda's adoption of her. 16. In the bell tower. 17. She was kidnapped by Hans. 18. Damian was shot while trying to rescue her from Hans. Lily stayed with him to help him recuperate and then learned that she was pregnant with his child. 19. Holden left town to seek treatment at an out-of-state clinic specializing in memory disorders. 20. On the kitchen floor in the Snyder farmhouse.

Paging Dr. Dixon: The Malpractice Suit

1. He had been shot by Hans. 2. John first tended to Hans, who had also been shot and whose wounds were more life-threatening than Eduardo's. 3. When Eduardo threatened to reveal a family secret Orlena didn't want revealed, she applied pressure to his gunshot wound until it opened up again and he bled to death. 4. Two million dollars. 5. After John was stricken with colon cancer the previous year, the insurance company had raised its rates to an amount John wouldn't pay. 6. Jessica Griffin. 7. When Rick suffered a heart attack, John performed CPR on him. 8. That John give up practicing medicine. 9. High school biology teacher. 10. On her deathbed, Orlena all but confessed to Lisa that she had killed Eduardo.

Whodunit and Whogotit?

1. Even though Gavin Kruger had been convicted of Carolyn Crawford's murder, suspicion remained that Carolyn's husband, Darryl, had done her in. In the end, Gavin himself did turn out to be the killer. 2. Although James Stenbeck had not really been killed, he'd done a good enough job faking it that Barbara Ryan went to prison for the murder. Years later, Paul killed his father (who was trying to kill Emily Stewart at the time), but was found

not guilty. 3. John Dixon faked his own murder to frame James Stenbeck. When John's ex-wife Dee Stewart went on trial, John revealed his charade, for which he was sentenced to community service. 4. Tad Channing had been killed by Detective Hal Munson's lover, Denise Darcy. 5. Royce Keller suffered from multiple personality disorder; one of his alternate personalities had accidentally killed Royce's sister Neal Alcott during an argument.

Lucinda to the Third Power

1. Sierra—biological; Lily—adopted; and Bianca—adopted.
2. Royce Keller, Samantha Markham, and Neal Alcott. Royce and Samantha are twins. 3. Jacabo Esteban, Martin Guest, and James Walsh. 4. Craig Montgomery, James Stenbeck, and Scott Eldridge.

Broadcast in Stereo

1. c   2. b   3. c   4. a   5. d   6. a   7. c   8. d   9. c   10. b   11. d (The CD was titled *A Soap Opera Christmas*.)   12. d

Simply Barbara

1. She slipped into bed with Tom while he was passed out drunk. When he woke up in the morning, Barbara convinced him that they had slept together.   2. Tonio was married to Lucinda's daughter Sierra.   3. Duncan was Shannon O'Hara's presumed-dead husband. Barbara brought him to town to prevent Shannon from marrying Brian McColl, whom Barbara wanted back.
4. Sabrina was a reminder that Bob Hughes had cheated on Barbara's mother Jennifer, to whom he was married at the time of Sabrina's conception.   5. That Margo Hughes had given birth to his son and was raising the boy, Adam, as Tom's son.   6. Hal learned that he was not the father of Barbara's baby daughter Jennifer.   7. The murder of Carolyn Crawford.   8. Hal had been working undercover to infiltrate a mob family. Although his cover had been compromised, Hal risked his life breaking into the family's safe to retrieve a photographic negative which was being using to blackmail Frannie's husband. When Barbara had

been told that Hal was subsequently killed by the mob, she held Frannie responsible. (Hal later turned out to be alive.) 9. Barbara wanted Hal to quit the police force, which she considered too dangerous a job for him. She figured that if he thought her life was in danger, he would agree to run security at her company. 10. Barbara had had an affair with Evan Walsh while separated from Hal. 11. None of them. She married James Stenbeck after Paul was born; she was never married to Darryl Crawford, Jennifer's father; and she conceived Hal's son William in between their marriages. 12. Simply Barbara and Barbara Ryan Originals.

The World of Eileen Fulton
1. a   2. b   3. d   4. c   5. d   6. c   7. a   8. b   9. b   10. d

Rosanna, Rosanna
1. During a business meeting with Alexander Cabot, Evan spotted Rosanna's picture on Alexander's desk and recognized her. Alexander told Evan that Rosanna was his daughter. 2. His company, Cabot Motors, manufactures automobiles. 3. Edwina told Evan that Alexander Cabot was his biological father, making Rosanna his half sister. Through a paternity test, Evan was able to prove that he was not Alexander Cabot's son. Ironically, Edwina married Alexander, making Rosanna Evan's stepsister. 4. Mike was the mechanic working on Rosanna's car. They got into an argument when she came to pick it up, and it wasn't ready. 5. Rosanna learned that her mother had abandoned her husband and her baby daughter Carly to run off and marry the wealthy Alexander Cabot. 6. Alexander Cabot suffered a heart attack while having an argument with Mike. As Alexander fell, he hit his head on an ashtray. Rosanna walked in to her father's hotel room to find her father on the ground, bleeding from his head, and Mike standing over him, holding the ashtray. Mike was subsequently arrested but eventually proven innocent by the autopsy. 7. Scott and Rosanna's newly discovered half sister Carly pretended that she had been kidnapped and tricked Rosanna into paying the $100,000 "ransom." 8. In a box of

Cracker Jacks.   9. Rosanna learned that Mike had slept with her sister Carly.   10. Gambling.

Social Issues of the Day
1. b   2. a   3. b   4. c   5. a   6. a   7. b   8. c   9. d   10. c

A Family Tree Grows in Oakdale
1. c   2. a (Tonio was engaged to Sabrina.)   3. d   4. b   5. d   6. b
7. c   8. a (Tom's father Bob is married to Andy's mother Kim.)
9. c   10. c

Current Events
1. John romanced Lisa into an engagement and then dumped her at the engagement party in front of all their friends and family members.   2. In a plane crash.   3. Samantha was also on the plane that crashed.   4. Hong Kong.   5. In a tree house Mark had built for Connor.   6. Cal fell out of the tree house.   7. Kim Hughes.   8. Mac died during surgery following a heart attack.   9. Higher-ups in the white supremacist organization had Jessica's sister Fiona arrested to blackmail Jessica into taking the case.   10. During a fight with her sister, Rosanna, at the Falcon Club, Carly lost her footing and fell overboard, which sent her into premature labor.

World History Final Exam
1. d   2. c   3. b   4. d   5. c   6. c   7. d   8. b   9. c   10. a   11. c   12. a
13. b   14. b   15. c   16. a   17. b   18. a   19. b   20. d   21. c   22. d
23. b   24. c   25. b   Bonus. c

Photo Quiz
1. Kim and Bob had each been married four times to other people before marrying each other.   2. My Cousin Vinnie.   3. Diana had made a play for both Steve and Craig. After Betsy married Craig, Diana lured Steve into marriage.   4. Dee Stewart.   5. Lady Bianca Scott.   6. Gunnar was the true Stenbeck heir. He had been switched at birth with James's real mother, Greta Aldrin.   7. Barney Miller.   8. Best Female Newcomer.   9. Three times.

More Citadel Entertainment Fun Facts and Interesting Trivia

Ask for any of these books at your bookstore. Or to order direct from the publisher, call 1-800-447-BOOK (MasterCard or Visa), or send a check or money order for the books purchased (plus $4.00 shipping and handling for the first book ordered and 75¢ for each additional book) to Carol Publishing Group, 120 Enterprise Avenue, Dept. 1808, Secaucus, NJ 07094.

The Critics Were Wrong: The Most Misguided Movie Reviews and Film Criticism Gone Wrong by Ardis Sillick & Michael McCormick $12.95 paper (#51722)

Film Flubs: Memorable Movie Mistakes by Bill Givens $7.95 paper (#51161)

Also Available:
Son of Film Flubs by Bill Givens $7.95 paper (#51279)

Film Flubs: The Sequel by Bill Givens $7.95 paper (#51360)

Final Curtain: Deaths of Noted Movie and TV Personalities by Everett G. Jarvis $17.95 paper (#51646)

The "Seinfeld" Aptitude Test by Beth B. Golub $8.95 paper (#51583)

701 Toughest Movie Trivia Questions of All Time by William MacAdams and Paul Nelson $9.95 paper (#51700)

Starfleet Academy Entrance Exam by Peggy Robin $9.95 paper (#51695)

The TV Theme Song Trivia Book by Vincent Terrace $9.95 paper (#51786)

1,201 Toughest TV Trivia Questions of All Time by Vincent Terrace $9.95 paper (#51730)

The Ultimate Clint Eastwood Trivia Book by Lee Pfeiffer & Michael Lewis $8.95 paper (#51789)

The Ultimate James Bond Trivia Book by Michael Lewis $8.95 paper (#51793)

The Ultimate John Wayne Trivia Book by Alvin H. Marill $9.95 paper (#51660)

What's Your "Cheers" I.Q.? by Mark Wenger $9.95 paper (#51780)

What's Your "Friends" I.Q.? by Stephen Spignesi $9.95 paper (#51776)

What's Your "Mad About You" I.Q.? by Stephen Spignesi $8.95 paper (#51682)

Prices subject to change; books subject to availability